Elementary Photographic Chemistry

Eastman Kodak Company
Rochester, N. Y.
1941

INTRODUCTION

Photography is so essentially a chemical process that every photographer should have an interest in the chemicals which he uses and in the reactions which they undergo.

This book is written in response to a demand for a simple account of photographic chemistry, for the practical photographer.

No attempt has been made to give the chemical theory in full, for which textbooks on chemistry should be consulted. In Chapter I, a statement is given only of the chemistry which is necessary to an understanding of the remainder of the book. In the same way reference should be made to photographic textbooks for general photographic practice.

To give the information about photographic chemicals which is necessary for their intelligent use, the properties of each of the more important chemicals are given in a separate paragraph, which is inserted in the section dealing with its use, in a distinct type face to facilitate reference. A table of solubilities of the chemicals in common photographic use is given at the end of the book. Practical information on preparing and using photographic solutions is given in Chapters VIII and IX. Chapter X contains a comprehensive formulary. Several useful indexes and tables are included at the back of the book.

No apology is necessary for the insistence placed on the need for pure chemicals and on the advantage to be gained by using the Eastman Tested Chemicals, which are specially purified and tested for photographic use.

EASTMAN KODAK COMPANY,
ROCHESTER, N. Y.

CONTENTS

Chapter	Page
I. An Outline of Elementary Chemistry	5
II. The Chemistry of Photographic Materials	12
III. The Chemistry of Development	17
IV. The Chemistry of Fixation	27
V. The Chemistry of Washing	32
VI. The Chemistry of Reduction and Intensification	36
VII. The Chemistry of Toning	42
VIII. Preparing Solutions	49
IX. Using Solutions	72
X. Formulas	90

INDEXES AND TABLES

Formula Index	145
Approximate Keeping Properties and Life of Developers, Rinse Baths and Fixing Baths	150
Equivalent Weights of Chemicals	153
Time-Temperature Development Tables	154
Table of Chemical Solubilities	156
Subject Index	158

CHAPTER I

AN OUTLINE OF ELEMENTARY CHEMISTRY

All substances are made by the combination in various proportions of a limited number of *elements*, of which about ninety exist. These elements combine in definite proportions to form bodies of fixed composition, which are termed *compounds*. Thus, one volume of the gaseous element hydrogen combines with one volume of the gaseous element chlorine to form two volumes of the compound hydrogen chloride gas. This combination can be represented by what is called a chemical equation. If we write H_2 for a molecule of hydrogen, Cl_2 for a molecule of chlorine and HCl for a molecule of hydrogen chloride, we can represent the combination by the equation:

$$H_2 + Cl_2 = 2\,HCl$$
Hydrogen   Chlorine   Hydrogen Chloride Gas

It will be seen that such an equation is really a shorthand method of stating what happens, the elements which take part in the combination being designated by letters. These letters which stand for the elements are called the "symbols" of the elements.

The elements which are of the greatest importance in photography and their symbols are:

Gases

Name	Symbol	Characteristic
Hydrogen	H	The lightest gas known.
Nitrogen	N	Forms 80% of the air. (Approx.)
Oxygen	O	Forms 20% of the air. (Approx.)
Chlorine	Cl	Greenish-yellow poisonous gas.
Bromine	Br	Poisonous brownish-red gas at high temperatures, liquid at ordinary temperatures.

Non-metallic Solids

Name	Symbol	Characteristic
Carbon	C	Occurs in three forms: diamond, graphite, and charcoal or amorphous carbon.
Boron	B	Brownish-black powder or yellowish-brown crystals.
Sulfur	S	Yellowish-white, brittle solid.
Iodine	I	Violet plate-like crystals, similar in chemical properties to chlorine and bromine.

5

Metallic Solids

Name	Symbol	Characteristic
Sodium	Na	Very light, attacked by moisture, kept under light oil.
Potassium	K	Very light, attacked by moisture, kept under light oil.
Calcium	Ca	Silvery white metal, attacked by moisture.
Aluminum	Al	Very light, white metal.
Iron	Fe	In the pure state it is called wrought-iron; when containing a small quantity of carbon it forms cast-iron and steel.
Copper	Cu	Reddish, tough metal.
Silver	Ag	White metal.
Platinum	Pt	Valuable white metal, very heavy.
Gold	Au	Reddish yellow metal, very heavy.
Mercury	Hg	White metallic liquid, very heavy.

These elements fall into two groups; those which are metals and those which are not metals. Apart from the appearance of the elements, the classification of an element in one of these two groups depends upon its relation to oxygen. Many of the elements when heated in the presence of oxygen will combine with it and will form what are called *oxides*. Thus, carbon will burn in oxygen and will form a gaseous compound of carbon with oxygen called *carbon dioxide*. Iron will burn in oxygen and form a solid iron oxide.

Oxides of Elements

Name	Symbol	Characteristic
Hydrogen oxide (water)	H_2O	Can be made by burning hydrogen in air or oxygen.

Acid Oxides

Carbon dioxide	CO_2	A heavy gas produced by burning carbon; for example, charcoal.
Nitric oxide	NO	Colorless gas, turns reddish-brown in contact with oxygen.
Sulfur dioxide	SO_2	Colorless gas. Produced by burning sulfur.

Basic Oxides

Aluminum oxide	Al_2O_3	White powder formed when aluminum is burned in the air.
Calcium oxide	CaO	Quicklime, obtained by heating chalk.
Iron oxide	Fe_2O_3	Red powder formed when iron rusts.
Mercuric oxide	HgO	Red powder formed by slow heating of mercury in the air.

OUTLINE OF ELEMENTARY CHEMISTRY

Many oxides are soluble in water, forming two classes of compounds, which are known respectively as *acids* and *bases*, the acid oxides being produced from the non-metallic elements and the basic oxides from the metallic elements. Thus, carbon, nitrogen and sulfur all form acid oxides which dissolve in water to form acids, while sodium, potassium and calcium form typical basic oxides which dissolve in water to form bases.

Bases are either alkaline or earthy, the alkaline bases being soluble, the earthy bases insoluble. The ordinary way of distinguishing between an acid and a base is to test the solution with a trace of certain dyes which change color according to whether the solution is acid or alkaline. Thus, if a piece of paper soaked in a solution of litmus, generally known as litmus paper, is put into a solution, it will turn red if the solution is acid, and blue if the solution is alkaline. Sodium forms an oxide which dissolves in water and makes a solution of basic caustic soda, the caustic soda having the formula NaOH, and being composed of sodium, oxygen and hydrogen. On the other hand, sulfur combines with oxygen and the oxide dissolves in water to form sulfurous acid, this having the formula H_2SO_3 and being formed by the combination of water, H_2O, with sulfur dioxide, SO_2. Thus:

$$SO_2 + H_2O = H_2SO_3$$
Sulfur Dioxide   Water   Sulfurous Acid

All acids contain hydrogen and this hydrogen can be replaced by a metal, forming a compound which is termed a "salt." Thus, if we have sulfuric acid and we dissolve a piece of iron in it, the iron will replace the hydrogen of the acid, which will be given off as bubbles of gas and a solution of the salt, iron sulfate, will be formed:

$$H_2SO_4 + Fe = FeSO_4 + H_2$$
Sulfuric Acid   Iron   Iron Sulfate   Hydrogen Gas

Salts are also formed by the direct union of an acid and a base. Thus, if we have caustic soda, NaOH, and sulfurous acid, H_2SO_3, they combine to form sodium sulfite, eliminating water. Thus:

$$2\,NaOH + H_2SO_3 = Na_2SO_3 + 2\,H_2O$$
Two parts of   Sulfurous Acid   Sodium Sulfite   Two parts
Caustic Soda   of Water

It will be seen that the sodium sulfite is formed by the combination of the base derived from sodium with the acid derived from sulfur.

Sometimes a non-metallic element forms two different oxides, and these in turn will form two different acids. When we burn sulfur in oxygen, for instance, each atom of sulfur combines with two atoms of oxygen and forms sulfur dioxide:

$$S \; + \; 2\,O \; = \; SO_2$$

and this dissolves in water to form sulfurous acid. If the sulfur dioxide is passed, with more oxygen over heated platinum, it is possible to make it combine with another atom of oxygen and form the compound sulfur trioxide, SO_3, and this dissolves in water and forms sulfuric acid:

$$SO_3 \; + \; H_2O \; = \; H_2SO_4$$

so that from sulfur we not only get sulfurous acid but a second acid—sulfuric acid.

Just as the hydrogen of sulfurous acid is replaced by sodium to form sodium sulfite, so the hydrogen of sulfuric acid is replaced by sodium to form sodium sulfate.

Sulfur Dioxide	SO_2	Sulfur Trioxide	SO_3
Sulfurous Acid	H_2SO_3	Sulfuric Acid	H_2SO_4
Sodium Sulfite	Na_2SO_3	Sodium Sulfate	Na_2SO_4

Salts are usually neutral to litmus paper, though sometimes they are somewhat acid or alkaline. But in addition to the neutral salts, an acid in which there are two hydrogen atoms can have one of them replaced by a metal instead of both, and in this case we get acid salts, which are equivalent in their behavior to a mixture of equal parts of the acid and the neutral salt. For instance, from sulfurous acid if we replace both the hydrogens, we get sodium sulfite—Na_2SO_3—but if we replace only one of the hydrogens, we get the compound $NaHSO_3$, which is called sodium acid sulfite, sodium hydrogen sulfite or, more usually, sodium bisulfite.

Sulfur forms a number of different acids. It forms not only acids from its two oxides SO_2 and SO_3, but it forms compound acids containing more than one atom of sulfur, and of these, one is of very great importance to the photographer, namely, thiosulfuric acid, which forms a sodium salt, sodium thiosulfate, $Na_2S_2O_3$. It will be seen that this compound differs from sodium sulfite in having two atoms of sulfur instead of one, and it is the compound, generally known as 'hypo," which is used for fixing photographic materials.

Some acids are formed not from oxides but by the direct combination of a non-metallic element with hydrogen, and of these the most important are the strong acids formed from chlorine, bromine and iodine, which three elements, because they occur in sea salt, are called halogens, from the Greek, meaning *salt producing*. Thus, chlorine combines directly with hydrogen to form hydrochloric acid, H Cl, and if the hydrogen of this is replaced by metals, we get chlorides, of which the best known is sodium chloride, Na Cl, which is common salt. Similarly, bromine combines with hydrogen to form hydrobromic acid, with which metals form bromides, and in the same way the iodides are formed from iodine.

The Halogens, Their Acids and Salts

Halogen Element		Acid		Sodium Salt
Cl	Chlorine	HCl	Hydrochloric Acid	NaCl	Sodium Chloride
Br	Bromine	HBr	Hydrobromic Acid	NaBr	Sodium Bromide
I	Iodine	HI	Hydriodic Acid	NaI	Sodium Iodide

Salts are soluble in water to different extents, the solubility depending upon the nature of the salt. (See Table of Chemical Solubilities, page 156.) Some, such as hypo, are extremely soluble, hypo being soluble in less than its own volume of water; while others are only slightly soluble or even almost completely insoluble, silver chloride, bromide and iodide being well known examples of very insoluble materials. A solution of a salt may be regarded as containing both the basic and the acid components of the salt in a more or less free condition. For instance, all copper salts in solution behave in much the same way, showing properties in common, due to the presence of the copper. In the same way all chlorides or sulfates show common properties in solution.

Now, when we mix two solutions of soluble salts, and the base of one can form an insoluble salt with the acid of the other, then this rearrangement will take place and the insoluble substance will be thrown out of solution as a precipitate. Thus, silver nitrate and sodium chloride are both very soluble in water, but when the solutions are mixed, the silver and the sodium change places so that silver chloride and sodium nitrate are formed, and the almost insoluble silver chloride is thrown out of the solution, leaving only the sodium nitrate behind.

$$\underset{\substack{\text{Silver Nitrate}\\ \text{Soluble}}}{\text{Ag NO}_3} + \underset{\substack{\text{Sodium Chloride}\\ \text{Soluble}}}{\text{Na Cl}} = \underset{\substack{\text{Silver Chloride}\\ \text{Insoluble}\\ \text{Precipitated}}}{\text{Ag Cl}} + \underset{\substack{\text{Sodium Nitrate}\\ \text{Soluble}}}{\text{Na NO}_3}$$

This "double decomposition" is the simplest kind of chemical reaction and is the one with which we are most familiar.

Other types of chemical reaction which are of great importance in photography are those of oxidation and reduction. The simplest example of oxidation is, of course, that in which an element combines with oxygen; but when an element forms two or more compounds with oxygen, then we are said to perform oxidation when we raise the element from the level of oxidation of one of its compounds to another level in which it is combined with more oxygen. For example, by the oxidation of sodium sulfite, Na_2SO_3, which is a compound formed from sulfur dioxide, SO_2, we get sodium sulfate Na_2SO_4, which is derived from sulfur trioxide, SO_3. This can be done by means of oxygen. If we pass air, which contains 20% of oxygen (the rest being chiefly nitrogen), through a sulfite solution, or even leave sodium sulfite exposed to the air for long periods, it will be oxidized into sulfate—

$$\underset{\text{Sodium Sulfite}}{Na_2SO_3} + \underset{\text{Oxygen}}{O} = \underset{\text{Sodium Sulfate}}{Na_2SO_4}$$

When metallic elements form two oxides with different amounts of oxygen, these two oxides will act as bases for two series of salts. Thus, iron forms

Ferrous salts derived from Fe O, and
Ferric salts derived from Fe_2O_3.

Thus, we have

Ferrous Chloride, Fe Cl_2, green crystals,
Ferric Chloride, Fe Cl_3, red-brown crystals.

Very often oxidation is accomplished not by the use of oxygen itself, but by the use of some substance which itself is a higher compound of oxygen, and which can be reduced to a lower compound of oxygen or to an element which contains no oxygen at all. Thus, for instance, when hydroquinone is oxidized, we get quinone, which we call the oxidation product of hydroquinone, but if we add sulfite to quinone, the quinone oxidizes the sulfite to sulfate and is itself reduced again to

OUTLINE OF ELEMENTARY CHEMISTRY

hydroquinone. In this case the sulfite acts as a *reducing agent*, reduction being the opposite to oxidation. Thus, a body which is easily oxidized will take the oxygen it needs from other substances and so act as a reducing agent. *Hydroquinone* is oxidized to *quinone*, which is reduced by sulfite to *hydroquinone*. Conversely, the *sulfite* is oxidized by the quinone to *sulfate*.

Similarly, if we add *ferric* salts to hydroquinone, they will oxidize it to *quinone* and will themselves be reduced to *ferrous* salts.

The term reduction is applied especially to the liberation of metallic elements from their compounds. If we heat mercuric oxide, the oxygen is driven off by the heat and the mercuric oxide is reduced to mercury. Generally, reduction cannot be accomplished by heat alone, and it is necessary to have some substance present which can be oxidized in order to reduce a compound. Thus, to reduce iron from its oxide, of which iron ore is chiefly composed, we heat it with charcoal or carbon, which is oxidized to form carbon dioxide and which reduces the iron oxide to metallic iron.

Chemical compounds consist of five great classes:

1. **ACIDS,** which are formed from non-metallic elements and which contain hydrogen replaceable by a metal;
2. **BASES,** which are formed from the metallic elements, and which, when soluble in water, are called alkalis;
3. **SALTS,** which are formed from the combination of an acid and a base;
4. **OXIDIZERS,** which are substances containing an excess of oxygen and which can give up this oxygen to another compound;
5. **REDUCERS,** which are greedy for oxygen and which take the oxygen away from any compound containing an available supply of it.

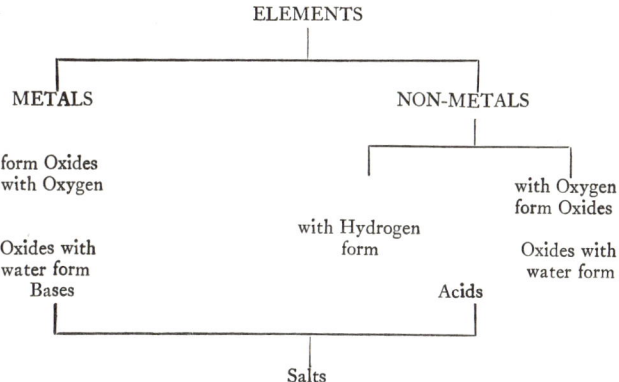

CHAPTER II

THE CHEMISTRY OF PHOTOGRAPHIC MATERIALS

The art of photography is founded upon the fact that the compounds of silver, and especially its compounds with chlorine, bromine and iodine, are sensitive to light.

The earliest photographs were made by coating paper with silver chloride and using this to form images by its darkening under the action of light, but the sensitiveness of the silver chloride was too slight to use it in this way to form images in the camera.

To get results which require less exposure to light, advantage is taken of the fact that it is not necessary for the light to do the whole work of forming the image; it is possible to expose the silver salt for only a short time to the light and then to continue the production of the image by chemical action, the process being termed "development."

Sensitive photographic materials therefore consist of paper, film, or glass coated with a layer in which is suspended the sensitive silver bromide or silver chloride. This layer is called the *emulsion*. This emulsion consists of a suspension of the silver salt in a solution of gelatin. It is made by soaking gelatin in water until it is swollen and then dissolving it by gently warming and stirring. The necessary bromide or chloride, e.g., potassium bromide or sodium chloride, is then added to the solution and dissolves in it. Meanwhile, the right quantity of silver nitrate to react with the quantity of salts used has been weighed out and is dissolved in water. The silver nitrate solution is then added slowly to the solution of gelatin and salt and produces in it a precipitate of the silver compound, the mixing being done in the darkroom, since the silver compound produced is sensitive to white light. If there were no gelatin in the solution the silver compound would settle down to the bottom and an emulsion would not be formed, but the gelatin prevents the settling so that as the silver nitrate is added a little at a time, the precipitated silver salt is uniformly distributed through the solution. If this emulsion is coated on a support, such as paper or film and then cooled, the gelatin will set to a jelly, and when the jelly

CHEMISTRY OF PHOTOGRAPHIC MATERIALS

is dried we get a smooth coating of dry emulsion of the sensitive silver compound.

Photographic materials which are to be developed must contain no excess of soluble silver and the emulsion must be made so that there is always an excess of bromide or chloride, since any excess of soluble silver will produce a heavy fog over the whole of the surface as soon as the material is placed in the developer. In the case of a printing-out paper, however, which is not used for development but which is printed out, a chloride emulsion is made with an excess of silver nitrate. This causes rapid darkening in the light, so that prints made upon a printing-out paper are not developed, the visible image being toned and fixed. A printing-out paper can be developed with certain precautions, such as by the use of acid developers or after treatment with bromide to remove the excess of silver nitrate.

In the early days of photography prints were usually made on printing-out papers, but at the present time most prints are made by the use of developing-out chloride and bromide papers, which are chemically of the same nature as the negative making materials and are coated with emulsions containing no free silver nitrate.

Negative making materials such as films and plates, always contain silver bromide with a small addition of silver iodide. The different degrees of sensitiveness are obtained by varying the temperature and the duration of heating which the emulsions undergo during manufacture, the most sensitive emulsions being heated to higher temperatures and for a longer time than the slower emulsions.

If a slow bromide emulsion is coated upon paper, the material is known as *bromide paper* and is used for printing, and especially for making enlargements. The less sensitive papers which are commonly used for contact printing by artificial light contain silver chloride in the place of silver bromide.

In order to obtain silver nitrate the first step is to dissolve metallic silver in nitric acid. The silver replaces the hydrogen of the acid and forms silver nitrate, the hydrogen liberated decomposing a further portion of the nitric acid and forming nitrogen peroxide and water. The silver nitrate is crystallized out of the solution in colorless, transparent flakes.

SILVER NITRATE for photographic use has to be extremely pure, and since metallic silver usually contains a small quantity of other metals, such as copper and lead, it is necessary to free it from these impurities. This is accomplished by recrystallization, so that the silver nitrate is finally obtained in a pure form.

In order to insure the purity of the silver nitrate which it uses, the Eastman Kodak Company prepares its own and is the largest maker of silver nitrate in the world.

Silver nitrate is very soluble in water. It attacks organic material, and blackens skin, wood, cloth, and other similar substances on exposure to light.

When a solution of silver nitrate is added to a solution of a bromide or chloride of another element, a reaction occurs and the insoluble silver bromide or chloride is precipitated. Thus, if we add silver nitrate to potassium bromide, the reaction occurs according to the following equation:

$$AgNO_3 \quad + \quad KBr \quad = \quad AgBr \quad + \quad KNO_3$$
Silver Nitrate   Potassium Bromide   Silver Bromide   Potassium Nitrate

The potassium nitrate formed remains in solution, but if the solution is at all concentrated, the silver bromide is thrown down to the bottom of the vessel as a thick, curdy precipitate.

The bromides and chlorides used in photography are chiefly the salts of potassium and sodium. Both the bromides and the chlorides are obtained from naturally occurring salt deposits, but, whereas these deposits consist chiefly of chlorides, they contain only a very small quantity of bromide, and bromide is therefore a very much more expensive material than chloride.

The elements chlorine, bromine and iodine are all obtained from natural salt or from the sea, iodine being derived from certain sea weeds which extract it from the sea water and thus make it available in a concentrated form. Chlorine is a yellowish-green gas, very suffocating and poisonous; bromine gives dark red fumes which are even more noxious than chlorine and condense to a liquid, and iodine forms shining, black crystalline flakes which on heating give a violet vapor. The chief chlorides, bromides and iodides used in photography are the following:

AMMONIUM CHLORIDE: White crystals soluble in water. Made from ammonia and hydrochloric acid. Should have no smell, and when evaporated by heat should leave no residue behind.

AMMONIUM BROMIDE: Very similar to the chloride, which is the only impurity likely to be present.

AMMONIUM IODIDE: Should consist of colorless crystals. Decomposes in light and is stained yellow by the iodine liberated. Very soluble in water and deliquescent (see p. 23). Soluble in alcohol.

CHEMISTRY OF PHOTOGRAPHIC MATERIALS

SODIUM CHLORIDE: Ordinary table salt is fairly pure sodium chloride and a very pure salt is easily obtained. The pure salt is stable and not deliquescent. Soluble in cold water (40°F.) (4°C.) to the extent of 31 ounces of salt to 100 fluid ounces of solution. Solubility increases very little on heating.

SODIUM BROMIDE: A white salt, similar to the chloride but more soluble. Is generally pure but may contain chloride.

POTASSIUM CHLORIDE: White salt, very similar to sodium chloride.

POTASSIUM BROMIDE: Occurs as colorless cubical crystals and is generally pure. To facilitate handling and weighing potassium bromide is usually supplied in the granular form. Very soluble in water.

POTASSIUM IODIDE: Similar to bromide. Very soluble. May contain as impurities carbonate, sulfate and iodate, but is usually pure. A solution of potassium iodide dissolves iodine, which is insoluble in water, and it is therefore used to prepare a solution of iodine.

The gelatin which is used to emulsify the sensitive silver salts is a very complex substance which is obtained from the bones and skins of animals. Gelatin has some curious and valuable properties. In cold water it does not dissolve but it swells as if, instead of the gelatin dissolving in the water, the water dissolves in the gelatin. If the water is heated, the gelatin will dissolve, and it can be dissolved to any extent. It cannot be said that there is a definite solubility of gelatin in water in the same sense as salts may be considered to have a definite solubility. As more gelatin is added, the solution becomes thicker. If the gelatin solution is heated, it will become thinner and less viscous when hot, and will thicken again as it cools, but it will remain thinner than if it had not been heated, so that the heating of the gelatin solution produces a permanent change in its properties. If a gelatin solution is cooled, the gelatin will not separate from the solution in a dry state but the whole solution will set to a jelly. If the jelly is heated again, it will melt, and a jelly can be melted and reset many times. During the treatment there will be produced a progressive change in the jelly, and if the process is continued long enough, the solution will refuse to set and will remain as a thick liquid.

Gelatin belongs to the class of substances which are called colloids, the name being derived from a Greek word meaning "gummy." When a gelatin jelly is dried it shrinks and forms a horny or glassy layer of the gelatin itself, smooth and rather brittle. This dry gelatin, when placed in water, will at once absorb the water and swell up again to form a jelly. This swelling and shrinking are of great importance in photography. When a photographic material with an emulsion made with gelatin is placed in water, the film will swell up and will continue to absorb more water and swell for a long time, finally becoming soft and even dissolving, the extent to which this occurs depending on the temperature and the nature of the solutions in which it is placed. A small quantity of either an acid or alkali will produce a considerable increase in the swelling, and since the developer is alkaline and the fixing bath is acid, both these solutions have a great tendency to swell the gelatin, especially when they are warm. In order to avoid difficulty from this source, gelatin emulsions have a hardener added before they are coated, gelatin being hardened and made more resistant to swelling by the addition of alum.

Under ordinary circumstances no difficulty is experienced by the photographer due to the softening of the gelatin, but when photographic materials are exposed to extreme temperatures, care must be taken in handling them. Hardening agents such as alum must be added to the fixing bath, and all solutions must be kept at the same temperature in order to avoid sudden contractions or expansions of the gelatin which may result in detaching the film from its support or in the production of reticulation, i.e., a coarse wrinkling all over the film.

CHAPTER III

THE CHEMISTRY OF DEVELOPMENT

When a light sensitive material is exposed for a short time to light, although the change which takes place may be so minute that it cannot be detected by any ordinary means, if the exposed material is placed in a chemical solution, which is termed the "developer," the chlorine or bromine is taken away from the silver, and the black metallic silver which remains behind forms the image. This image is, of course, made up of grains, because the original emulsion contains the silver bromide in the form of microscopic crystals, and when the bromide is taken away from each of these, the crystal breaks up and a tiny coke-like mass of metallic silver remains behind in exactly the same position as the bromide crystal from which it was formed, so that, whereas the original emulsion consisted of microscopic crystalline grains of the sensitive silver salt, the final image consists of equally microscopic grains of black metallic silver. This removal of the bromide from the metallic silver is known chemically as *reduction*. (It must be remembered that chemical reduction has nothing to do with the photographic operation known as the reducing of a negative; that is, the weakening of an over-dense negative, where the word simply refers to the removal of the silver and is not used in the chemical sense.)

Chemical reducers are substances which have an affinity for oxygen and which can liberate the metals from their salts, such as the charcoal which, as explained in Chapter I, is used to reduce iron from its ore. A developing solution is therefore one which contains a chemical reducer. All substances which are easily oxidized are, however, not developers, since in order that a reducer may be used as a photographic developer it is necessary that it should be able to reduce exposed silver bromide but should not affect unexposed silver bromide, so that its affinity for oxygen must be within certain narrow bounds; it must be a sufficiently strong reducer to reduce the exposed silver salt, and at the same time must not affect that which has not been exposed. For practical purposes the developing agents are limited to a very few substances, almost all of which are chemically derived from benzene, the light oil which is distilled from coal tar.

18 ELEMENTARY PHOTOGRAPHIC CHEMISTRY

The commonest developing agents are pyrogallic acid (pyro or pyrogallol), hydroquinone, Elon, glycin-para-aminophenol, and di-aminophenol.

PYROGALLIC ACID (pyro or pyrogallol) is made from gallic acid, which is obtained from gall nuts imported from China. The gall nuts are fermented to obtain the gallic acid, and the gallic acid is then heated in a still from which the pyrogallic acid is distilled. Pyrogallic acid is made in two forms: (1) a flaky powder form, usually sold under the name of Resublimed Pyro, and (2) a crystal form. The powdered or resublimed form of Pyrogallic Acid is very light and fluffy and when a package is opened in the darkroom or studio, fine particles fly about and are likely to settle on paper or plates, producing spots on the photographs. For this reason, the Eastman Kodak Company manufactures and supplies a very pure pyrogallic acid in the crystal form, which can be handled without any danger of the particles flying about and giving trouble.

HYDROQUINONE is made from benzene which is first converted into aniline and then oxidized. Although it is somewhat less powerful as a reducing agent than pyro, it has less propensity to give stain and when used in conjunction with Elon it is a very useful developer, in fact, it is a constituent of the majority of the better known commercial developers in use today. It keeps very well when used in tank developers because it does not oxidize as readily as pyro and is generally used in motion picture work. Its purity is very important and Eastman Tested Hydroquinone, manufactured by the Company, may be relied upon for all formulas.

Some time after pyrogallic acid and hydroquinone were in general use by photographers, there were introduced a number of new developing agents made from coal tar, which are very useful as supplements to the older developers. Several of these are based on a substance called *para-aminophenol*, which is made in the manufacture of dyes. When para-aminophenol is treated with methyl alcohol the methyl part of the alcohol attaches itself to it and forms a compound called *methyl-para-aminophenol*, which is a more active developing agent than the para-aminophenol itself. Another developing agent of the same type is *di-aminophenol*, which is prepared in a way similar to para-aminophenol.

Para-aminophenol, methyl-para-aminophenol and di-aminophenol are all bases and the developing agents are their salts, the hydrochloride of para-aminophenol, and of di-aminophenol being used, and the sulfate of methyl-para-aminophenol.

Para-AMINOPHENOL HYDROCHLORIDE is made by combining para-aminophenol with hydrochloric acid and keeps better than para-aminophenol itself. This material should be light in color, freely soluble in water, and should burn entirely when heated to redness, leaving little or no ash behind. The para-aminophenol hydrochloride manufactured by the Eastman Kodak Company as *Kodelon* is of a high degree of purity.

CHEMISTRY OF DEVELOPMENT

MONOMETHYL Para-AMINOPHENOL SULFATE manufactured and sold by the Eastman Kodak Company under the name of *Elon*. Monomethyl para-aminophenol sulfate is distinguished sharply from para-aminophenol hydrochloride by the fact that it is soluble in its own weight of cool, strong hydrochloric acid, whereas the para-aminophenol hydrochloride is insoluble.

Di-AMINOPHENOL HYDROCHLORIDE is sold by the Eastman Kodak Company under the name of Acrol. It is a steel gray powder, darkening easily in the air and is oxidized so rapidly in solution that it is usual to dissolve it only when required for use.

Para-HYDROXYPHENYL GLYCIN or GLYCIN is manufactured and sold by the Eastman Kodak Company under the name *Athenon*. It is made by the interaction of para-aminophenol and monochloracetic acid. It forms lustrous flaky crystals, nearly white in color, which are difficult to dissolve in water but readily soluble in weakly alkaline solutions. The crystals should burn entirely when heated to redness, leaving little or no ash behind. Athenon is a useful developing agent for compounding developers which give warm tones on chlorobromide papers.

Different reducing agents behave differently as developers. We cannot use Elon in the place of hydroquinone and get the same effect. An image developed with Elon comes up very quickly and gains density slowly, while the hydroquinone image comes up very slowly but gains density steadily and rapidly. A very little change in the temperature affects hydroquinone greatly and affects Elon very little, and in the same way a small quantity of sodium or potassium bromide affects hydroquinone and does not affect Elon nearly so much. These differences in the developing agents depend upon the chemical nature of the substances themselves, and the particular property to which these differences are due is called the "reduction potential" of the developer.

The reduction potential alone does not determine the speed with which the developer develops the image, because this depends chiefly upon the rate at which the developer diffuses into the film and on the quantity of developing agent and other substances in the developer. A high reduction potential enables a developer to continue to develop more nearly at a normal rate under adverse circumstances, such as at a low temperature or in the presence of bromide. The reduction potential of a developer, in fact, may be compared to the horse-power of an automobile which for other reasons than the power of its engine is limited in speed. If we have two automobiles and they are confined to a maximum speed of twenty miles an hour, then on level roads the one with the more powerful engine may be no faster than that with a weaker engine, but in a high wind or on a more hilly road the more powerful engine will allow the automobile to keep its speed, while the machine with the weaker engine will be forced to go more slowly. We could, indeed, measure the horse-power of an automobile by the maximum grade which it could climb at a uniform speed of 20 miles an hour.

In development, the analogy to the hill is the addition of bromide to the developer, since the addition of bromide greatly retards development, and it is found that the higher the reduction potential of a developer, the more bromide is required to produce a given effect. If we measure the developing agents in this way, we shall find that hydroquinone has the lowest reduction potential, then glycin, then para-aminophenol, then pyro, and finally Elon, which has the highest. Hydroquinone has so low a potential that it is rarely used alone but is generally used with Elon. Para-aminophenol can be substituted for Elon but more para-aminophenol has to be used in order to produce a developer of the same strength. Developers with a high reduction potential such as Elon, make the image flash up all over at once, because they start development very quickly even in the lesser exposed portions of the emulsion, while developers of low reduction potential, like pyro and especially hydroquinone, bring up the highlights of the image first and the shadows do not fully appear until the highlights are somewhat developed.

Most developing agents cannot develop at all when used by themselves. With the exception of di-aminophenol, developing agents, in order to do their work, must be in an alkaline solution, and the energy depends upon the amount of alkali present. The developers of higher reduction potential, which bring up the image very quickly, require less alkali than those of lower reduction potential. For instance, hydroquinone is often used with caustic alkalis, while the other developing agents require only the weaker carbonated alkali.

The quantity of alkali governs the energy of a developer, and if too much alkali is present, the developer will tend to produce chemical fog, while if too little alkali is present, it will be slow in its action. Alkalis also soften the gelatin of the emulsion, and consequently too alkaline a developer will produce over-swelling and will give trouble with frilling or blisters in warm weather.

The alkalis most commonly used in development are of two kinds: the caustic alkalis and the carbonated alkalis.

Caustic alkalis are produced when the metal itself reacts with water, the metals from which the alkalis generally used are derived being potassium and sodium. These metals are so easily oxidized that they have to be preserved from all contact with air or water by immersion in light oil or gasoline.

If we take a small piece of sodium and place it on the surface of water in a dish, it will react with the water with great violence, melting with the heat produced and sputtering about the surface; while if we restrict its movement, the development of heat will be so great that the hydrogen produced will burst into flame. In the case of potassium, the reaction is even more violent than with sodium and is always accompanied by flame. The reaction may be represented by the equation—

$$\underset{\text{Sodium}}{Na} + \underset{\text{Water}}{H_2O} = \underset{\text{Sodium Hydroxide}}{NaOH} + \underset{\text{Hydrogen}}{H}$$

the sodium combining with the water to form caustic soda and liberating hydrogen, which comes off as gas, and, as has already been stated, catches fire and burns in the air. This is, of course, not the method by which the alkalis are actually produced. As a matter of fact, the metals are produced by electrolysis of the melted alkali.

SODIUM HYDROXIDE (CAUSTIC SODA) is made either by the passage of an electric current through a solution of common salt, when the soda separates at one electrode and chlorine gas is liberated at the other, or from sodium carbonate, which is causticized by means of lime. Lime is calcium oxide and is prepared by heating limestone, which is calcium carbonate, the carbon dioxide being driven off from the limestone by the heat. When the lime is added to sodium carbonate, the lime removes the carbon dioxide from the carbonate, and leaves the sodium hydrate in the solution, which is then evaporated to get the solid substance. At present, caustic soda is easily obtained in a very pure state, and there is usually no difficulty in getting good caustic soda for photographic work. It must be protected from the air, since it easily absorbs moisture and carbon dioxide. As its name indicates, it is very caustic and attacks the skin, clothing, etc.

POTASSIUM HYDROXIDE (CAUSTIC POTASH) is very similar to caustic soda and is prepared in the same way. Fifty-six parts of caustic potash are chemically equivalent to forty parts of caustic soda.

Both caustic soda and caustic potash should be dissolved in cold water when solutions of either chemical are prepared, because on mixing, considerable heat is evolved and the solution, if too hot, is apt to boil and spatter on the hands or face causing serious burns.

An alkali which was often used with pyrogallol in the early days of photography, but which is rarely used nowadays, is ammonia. Nitrogen combines with three times its volume of hydrogen to form a gas, NH_3. This gas is known as ammonia and is very soluble in water, its solution being strongly alkaline. Ammonia combines directly with acids to form salts which are analogous to the salts of sodium and potassium. Thus with hydrochloric acid it forms ammonium chloride, which is similar to sodium chloride and potassium chloride:

$$\underset{\text{Ammonia}}{NH_3} + \underset{\text{Hydrochloric Acid}}{HCl} = \underset{\text{Ammonium Chloride}}{NH_4Cl}$$

Ammonia is a somewhat weaker alkali than soda or potash but stronger than the carbonates. For use in development it has the disadvantage that being used in the form of a solution of a gas its strength is somewhat uncertain and variable, the ammonia escaping from the solution. Also, it is a solvent of silver bromide and tends to produce colored stains which are not so easily produced with other alkalis.

AMMONIA SOLUTION is commercially prepared from the ammoniacal liquor obtained in the distillation of coal for coal gas. The liquor is neutralized with sulfuric acid, the ammonium sulfate crystallized out, and the ammonia gas liberated from the sulfate with lime and led into water, in which it dissolves. The solution is usually free from impurities.

Ammonia solutions are prepared commercially in two strengths, "ammonia water," containing 10% of ammonia gas by weight and having a specific gravity of 0.96, and "strong ammonia water" containing 28% of ammonia by weight and having a specific gravity of 0.90.

The alkalis generally used for photographic work are not the caustic alkalis but the carbonates, which are salts of carbonic acid, H_2CO_3. Carbonic acid is a very weak acid, so that in solution the carbonates are not neutral but alkaline because of the predominance of the strong base over the weak acid, the carbonate being, to some extent, split up into the bicarbonate or acid carbonate and the caustic alkali. The use of a carbonate in development therefore represents a sort of reservoir of alkali, only a small quantity of alkali being present at any time, but more being generated by dissociation of the carbonate as it is used up. If instead of using carbonate we were to use for development a solution containing a proportional quantity of caustic alkali, we should have only a small quantity of alkali present, and it would soon be exhausted. The use of carbonate, therefore, enables us to employ a small concentration of alkali and yet to keep that concentration nearly constant during use.

When a salt is dissolved in water at a high temperature until no more will dissolve and then the solution is allowed to cool, the salt will generally be deposited in crystals; sometimes, as in the case of silver nitrate, the crystals consist of the pure substance, but more often each part of the salt combines with one or more parts of water to form the crystals. This combined water is called "water of crystallization." Thus, crystals of sodium carbonate formed from a cool solution contain ten parts of water to one of carbonate, and their composition should be written:

$$Na_2CO_3 \cdot 10H_2O$$

When exposed to the air chemicals often either absorb or give up water. Those which absorb water are said to be "hygroscopic," and if they absorb so much that they dissolve and form a solution they are said to be "deliquescent." Chemicals which give up water to the air, so that the crystals break down and become covered with powder, are called "efflorescent."

SODIUM CARBONATE is usually sold in three forms: (1) crystals with ten parts of water, $Na_2CO_3.10H_2O$, containing 37% of sodium carbonate, usually known as washing soda; (2) crystals with one part of water, $Na_2CO_3.H_2O$, containing 85% of sodium carbonate, and known as monohydrated sodium carbonate; and (3) the dry particles containing 98-99% of sodium carbonate. In the manufacture of sodium carbonate, salt solution (sodium chloride) containing a small amount of ammonia is treated with carbon dioxide gas, forming ammonium chloride which remains in solution, and sodium bicarbonate, $NaHCO_3$, which precipitates. The bicarbonate is heated until half of the carbonic acid is driven off, leaving crude sodium carbonate, which, at this stage, is known as "soda ash." This soda ash is then dissolved in water, filtered to remove any insoluble impurity which may be present, and the filtered solution then allowed to crystallize. These crystals contain ten parts of water but are quite unstable, for if allowed to stand in the air, they rapidly lose a portion of this water so that their composition is continually changing. If, however, the filtered solution of sodium carbonate is evaporated, crystals of sodium carbonate containing one part of water will be deposited from the hot solution. These crystals are the monohydrated form, which is relatively stable. If, on the other hand, the filtered solution of sodium carbonate is again treated with carbon dioxide gas, a very pure form of sodium bicarbonate is precipitated from which half of the carbonic acid may be removed by heating. There remains a very pure form of sodium carbonate containing no water, which is known as "Sodium Carbonate, desiccated." The exact amount of heating is very important, for if the temperature is too low or if it is not heated for a sufficient length of time, some bicarbonate will be left in the product; while, on the other hand, if the temperature is too high, or the material is heated for too long a period of time, the sodium carbonate will contain some caustic soda.

The preparation of sodium carbonate is given the greatest attention by the Eastman Kodak Company. The product is supplied under the name "Sodium Carbonate, desiccated, (E.K.Co.)" and is specially prepared for compounding photographic developers. Experiments have shown that, when stored with moderate care in closed containers, the desiccated sodium carbonate is quite stable and will keep over long periods of time without any appreciable change in its composition.

If it is desired to substitute the monohydrated variety for the desiccated, in a formula calling for the latter, it is necessary to increase the quantity of desiccated carbonate by 17%, that is; if a formula calls for 100 grams (3 ozs. 145 grains) of desiccated sodium carbonate, then 117 grams (3 ozs. 400 grains) of monohydrated carbonate would be required.

POTASSIUM CARBONATE is sometimes used instead of sodium carbonate in developer formulas. Although it is more soluble than sodium carbonate, it has the disadvantages of being more expensive and absorbs water very readily. It must, therefore, be kept in well-sealed bottles.

Another alkali which is used extensively is borax. This is a mild alkali, suitable for compounding developers of low activity for development of miniature amateur negatives, professional portrait negatives, and motion picture negatives, especially variable density sound records.

BORAX or SODIUM TETRABORATE is prepared from certain calcium ores by first roasting, then boiling in sodium carbonate and bicarbonate solution, and finally crystallizing in large iron vats. A new source of borax discovered in Kern County, California in 1926 is virtually pure sodium borate and requires only dissolving, filtering, and recrystallizing to prepare it for the market. The pure salt forms large crystals readily soluble in hot water. It is used in developers of low activity and in acid hardeners for prints which are to be dried on belt driers. Borax is also added to gold toning baths to make them alkaline and to increase the rate of deposition of the gold. (See page 42.)

One of the disadvantages of the carbonated alkalies is their tendency to cause blister formation within the gelatin layer, as a result of the release of carbon dioxide gas, when the alkaline developer is neutralized with an acid hardening fixing bath. This trouble is particularly serious in summer months when temperature control of solutions becomes more difficult. Blister formation can be avoided entirely by using a new alkali, known as *Kodalk*, which was developed by the Kodak Research Laboratories and introduced in 1934. With increasing concentration of alkali, the activity of an MQ developer does not change as rapidly with Kodalk as when carbonate is used. This is an advantage because it is possible, therefore, to control precisely the activity of a weakly alkaline developer by varying the concentration of Kodalk. Also the average potassium alum-acid fixing bath does not sludge as readily with developers containing Kodalk as with developers containing carbonate. Kodalk dissolves readily in water and does not cake. Formulas are given on pages 92, 93, 97, 98 and 99 for this alkali for use with professional films and plates, roll films and film packs.

Owing to the fact that developers are necessarily substances which have a great affinity for oxygen and that the

CHEMISTRY OF DEVELOPMENT

air contains oxygen, developing solutions containing only the developing agent and alkali would be rapidly spoiled from oxidation by the air. In order to make the developer keep there is added to the developing solution, in addition to the reducing agent and alkali, some sodium sulfite. Sodium sulfite has a very strong affinity for oxygen, being easily oxidized to sodium sulfate (see page 10), so that it protects the developer from the oxygen of the air, thus acting as a "preservative." This action of the sulfite is very easily seen with the pyrogallol developer. The oxidation product of pyrogallol is yellow, and this oxidation product which is formed in development is deposited in the film along with the silver, so that if we use a pyrogallol developer without sulfite we shall get a very yellow negative, the image consisting partly of silver and partly of the oxidized pyrogallol. If we use sulfite in the developer, the image will be much less yellow because the pyrogallol will be prevented from oxidizing, the sulfite being oxidized instead, and finally if we add a great deal of sulfite, we shall get almost as blue an image as with Elon, the oxidation product of which is not deposited in a colored form with the silver.

SODIUM SULFITE is prepared by blowing sulfur dioxide gas into a given volume of a strong solution of sodium carbonate, until it has become saturated, after which an equal volume of sodium carbonate solution of the same strength is added. This solution when cooled, deposits crystals of sodium sulfite containing seven parts of water to one of sulfite ($Na_2SO_3.7H_2O$). These crystals contain 50% dry sulfite and give up their water of crystallization very readily on heating to form the desiccated product. The tested sodium sulfite supplied by the Eastman Kodak Company is the desiccated salt and is of a high degree of purity.

Sodium forms a number of compounds with sulfurous acid in addition to sodium sulfite itself. Thus there is sodium acid sulfite or bisulfite, $NaHSO_3$, which may be regarded as a compound of sodium sulfite with sulfurous acid:

$$Na_2SO_3 + H_2SO_3 = 2\,NaHSO_3$$
Sodium Sulfite   Sulfurous Acid   Sodium Bisulfite

Another, sodium metabisulfite, is a compound of sodium sulfite with sulfur dioxide:

$$Na_2SO_3 + SO_2 = Na_2S_2O_5$$
Sodium Sulfite   Sulfur Dioxide   Sodium Metabisulfite

Ordinary commercial bisulfite has been shown by analysis to consist chiefly of metabisulfite which is converted into bisulfite when dissolved in water. Commercially dry sodium bisulfite is supplied by the Eastman Kodak Company in a very pure form as one of its Tested Chemicals. It may be used with entire confidence when mixing formulas calling for either metabisulfite or bisulfite.

POTASSIUM METABISULFITE is often used as a preservative. It forms good crystals and is convenient to use but is rather costly in comparison with sodium bisulfite.

SODIUM BISULFITE, when pure, is a white salt which has an acid reaction, often containing a slight excess of sulfur dioxide. Since sodium sulfite is an alkaline salt, owing to the predominance of the strong base soda, over the weak sulfurous acid, a neutral solution can be produced by adding a small quantity of bisulfite to sulfite, and this neutral solution has found extensive application as a preservative for a pyro developer. Bisulfite is used occasionally as a preservative for fixing baths, supplying both the sulfite and the acid necessary.

It is difficult to prepare bisulfite free from iron, and any iron in the bisulfite produces a dark color when used for making up a pyro solution.

It is often customary to substitute sodium bisulfite for potassium metabisulfite weight for weight. It really comes down to a matter of dollars and cents because either chemical is quite satisfactory for the purpose but, as a rule, sodium bisulfite ranges in cost from *one-third* to *one-half* that of potassium metabisulfite.

Since sodium bisulfite may be considered as a compound of sodium sulfite and sulfurous acid, while sodium sulfite is alkaline, bisulfite is preferable as a preservative in the case of a two-solution developer, since oxidation progresses less readily in acid than in alkaline solution.

In the case of a one-solution developer containing, say, sodium sulfite, sodium bisulfite and sodium carbonate, the bisulfite is converted to sulfite by the sodium carbonate according to the following equation:

$$NaHSO_3 \; + \; Na_2CO_3 \; = \; Na_2SO_3 \; + \; NaHCO_3$$
Sodium Bisulfite   Sodium Carbonate   Sodium Sulfite   Sodium Bicarbonate

The sodium bisulfite neutralizes or destroys an equivalent quantity of sodium carbonate, thus reducing the proportion of alkali and therefore exerts an apparent restraining action, while the developer apparently keeps longer because some of the carbonate has been destroyed.

It might be thought from the above equation that it would be as effective and perhaps simpler to use only sodium sulfite instead of sulfite and bisulfite, but experiments have shown that the bicarbonate formed, acts as an anti-fogging agent.

A further discussion of the properties of developers is given under Chapter IX, page 72.

CHAPTER IV

THE CHEMISTRY OF FIXATION

After development, the emulsion contains, in addition to the developed silver image, all of the unexposed and undeveloped grains of silver bromide, which will darken if exposed to light and so cover up the desired image. In order to make the image permanent, it is necessary to "fix" the negative or print by removing the unused silver salts without affecting the developed image. There are only a few substances which will dissolve silver bromide, and the one which is universally used in modern photography is sodium thiosulfate, $Na_2S_2O_3$, which is known to photographers as hyposulfite of soda, or more usually as hypo, though the name hyposulfite of soda is used by chemists for another substance.

SODIUM THIOSULFATE or HYPO can be made by boiling together sodium sulfite and sulfur, the sulfur combining with the sodium sulfite according to the equation.

$$Na_2SO_3 \quad + \quad S \quad = \quad Na_2S_2O_3$$
Sodium Sulfite   Sulfur   Hypo

In practice it is generally made from calcium sulfite residues, the calcium thiosulfate being then converted into the sodium salt by treatment with sodium sulfate. The hypo comes on the market in clear crystals and is usually fairly pure, any foreign substance present being more often due to accidental contamination than to its chemical nature and consisting of dirt, straw or wood dust due to careless handling. Sometimes, however, the hypo contains calcium thiosulfate, which decomposes much more readily than the sodium salt. On the whole it is not difficult to obtain good hypo; the Eastman Tested Hypo is prepared in the form of prismatic crystals, easy to dissolve, and free from accidental contamination.

In the process of fixation the silver bromide is dissolved in the hypo by combining with it to form soluble complex thiosulfates of silver and sodium.

In its simplest form, a fixing bath consists merely of a solution of hypo which can dissolve the unused silver bromide. However, it is also desirable that the fixing bath should be able to neutralize the alkaline developer solution contained in the developed negative or print, in order to stop the development quickly and uniformly and thus prevent uneven development, and to avoid the danger of stains from colored materials produced by oxidation of the developer which has accumulated in the bath.

In order to prevent the gelatin from swelling and softening in the wash water, it is also usual to add to the fixing bath some hardening agent, such as potassium alum or chrome alum, to harden the gelatin, and these agents also require an acid solution. Unfortunately, however, acids tend to decompose hypo, causing the solution to become milky because of the precipitation of sulfur. This is because the acid converts the sodium thiosulfate into the free thiosulfuric acid, and this substance is quite unstable, decomposing into sulfurous acid and sulfur according to the equation:

$$\underset{\text{Thiosulfuric Acid}}{H_2S_2O_3} = \underset{\text{Sulfurous Acid}}{H_2SO_3} + \underset{\text{Sulfur}}{S}$$

The change of thiosulfate into sulfite and sulfur is reversible, since, if sulfite and sulfur are boiled together in alkaline solution, thiosulfate is formed, so that while acids liberate sulfur from the hypo, sulfite combines with the sulfur to form hypo again. Consequently, acid decomposition of the hypo can be prevented if there is enough sulfite present, since the sulfite works in the opposite direction to the acid. An acid fixing bath, therefore, is preserved from decomposition by the sulfite, which also helps to prevent the oxidation of developer carried over into it. Thus, the practical fixing bath usually contains in addition to the hypo, an acid to stop the development, sulfite to prevent decomposition of the hypo, and a hardening agent for the gelatin.

The developer which is carried over into the fixing bath is, however, alkaline and consequently a considerable quantity of acid is required in a fixing bath which is used for any length of time, since if only a small quantity is present, it will soon be neutralized by the developer carried over and a sludge of aluminum sulfite will be precipitated. We are, therefore, in the difficult position that a large quantity of acid is required, and yet the fixing bath must not be strongly acid. The solution of the difficulty is found by taking advantage of the fact that there are some acids which are very weak in their acidity and yet can neutralize alkali in the same way as a strong acid, so that a large quantity of these acids can be added without making the bath so acid that sulfur is precipitated.

The strength of an acid depends upon the fact that when it is dissolved in water some of the hydrogen contained in it dissociates from the acid and remains in the solution in an active form, and the acidity of the solution depends upon the proportion of the hydrogen which is dissociated into this active form. The quantity of alkali which the acid can neutralize, however, depends upon the total quantity of the hydrogen present, and not on the dissociated portions only.

Since a large quantity of a weak acid is required, one of the best acids for the purpose is acetic acid.

ACETIC ACID was formerly prepared from vinegar obtained from the fermentation of apple juice. It is now prepared, however, from the acid liquors obtained by the destructive distillation of wood, or synthetically from acetylene. The acid liquors are neutralized with lime to form calcium acetate and evaporated to dryness. The crude acetic acid is freed from the calcium acetate by the addition of sulfuric acid and is redistilled until the proper degree of purity has been reached. The acetic acid will then contain not less than 99.5% of acid and is known as glacial acetic acid, because at moderately low temperatures it solidifies. To eliminate possible contamination, Eastman Kodak Company's tested glacial acetic acid is distilled in glass equipment. By diluting three parts of pure glacial acetic acid with eight parts of water, 28% acetic acid may be prepared.

The compound, sodium bisulfite, $NaHSO_3$, is intermediate between sodium sulfite and sulfurous acid, and is, therefore, equal in acidity to a mixture of equal proportions of these two substances. It makes a satisfactory acid fixing bath but does not give quite as good a reserve of available acid in the bath as acetic acid does. This is of importance particularly in connection with the hardening agent used in the fixing bath. A satisfactory non-hardening acid fixing bath can be prepared, however, by adding sulfite and bisulfite to hypo (see Formula F-24, page 119).

The commonest hardening agent is potassium alum, the alums having the property of tanning gelatin.

ALUMS (as used in photography) are compounds or double salts of aluminum sulfate or chromium sulfate with sodium, potassium or ammonium sulfate. They have the general formula R_2SO_4, $M_2(SO_4)_3 \cdot 24H_2O$, where R may be an alkali metal or the ammonium radical, and M is chromium or aluminum. If the hydrogen in sulfuric acid be replaced by potassium, we get potassium sulfate, K_2SO_4, while if it be replaced by aluminum, we get aluminum sulfate, $Al_2(SO_4)_3$. The aluminum sulfate combines with other sulfates to form the alums, of which the commonest are potassium alum and ammonium alum. Sodium alum does not crystallize well, but the potassium and ammonium salts crystallize in large, clear crystals. They are almost always sold in the form of very fine crystals, to facilitate weighing and to prevent lumping which occurs with powdered alums.

POTASSIUM CHROME ALUM, K_2SO_4, $Cr_2(SO_4)_3 \cdot 24H_2O$, which is often used in the place of ordinary alum, does not contain any aluminum in spite of its name. It is a compound sulfate of potassium sulfate with chromium sulfate, of which the formula is $Cr_2(SO_4)_3$, the chromium taking the place of the aluminum present in aluminum sulfate. Chrome alum is prepared commercially in large quantities and of a high degree of purity. It occurs as violet crystals soluble in water, its solution in cold water being violet but going green on heating owing to the change in the composition of the salt.

AMMONIUM CHROME ALUM (NH$_4$)$_2$SO$_4$, Cr$_2$(SO$_4$)$_3$. 24H$_2$O, is chemically very similar to potassium chrome alum except that it is the compound of ammonium sulfate with chromium sulfate. Ammonium chrome alum is sometimes available on the market at a slightly lower price than the other alums, but for greatest efficiency and avoidance of trouble from stains, the use of potassium alum or chromium alum is to be preferred.

With fixing baths containing acetic acid, potassium alum, sodium sulfite and hypo, the range of acidity throughout which satisfactory hardening is maintained, is rather limited. When the acidity varies much above or below this range, the bath does not harden at all and when too alkaline, a sludge of basic aluminum sulfite is precipitated rendering the bath useless. If boric acid is added to a fixing bath of this type, however, the range of acidity over which good hardening exists is extended considerably and the sludging tendency of the bath is greatly diminished. (See Formulas F-5 and F-25, pages 115 and 118.)

BORIC ACID is prepared by treating a hot water solution of sodium borate with sulfuric or hydrochloric acid, allowing the resulting solution to cool, whereupon the white crystals of boric acid separate out. These are purified by recrystallization. Boric acid is also obtained by concentrating and purifying the dissolved acid contained in the vapors which issue from fumaroles in the marshes of Tuscany, Italy.

Chrome alum fixing baths are usually compounded with sulfuric acid (and sulfite) rather than acetic acid commonly used with potassium alum fixing baths. In the presence of sodium sulfite, a plain solution of chrome alum loses its hardening properties somewhat rapidly. Therefore if the sulfite content of a chrome alum fixing bath is too high or the chrome alum concentration too low, the bath loses its hardening properties whether in use or not. When properly compounded, however, the hardening properties and useful life of a chrome alum fixing bath compare favorably with those of a potassium alum fixing bath.

Chrome alum is also useful as a hardening bath between developing and fixing. A plain solution of chrome alum retains its hardening properties indefinitely, though with use when developer is carried over by the plates and films, the hardening properties of the bath fall off owing to the presence of sodium sulfite in the developer.

Formalin is sometimes suggested as a hardening agent in fixing baths for hot weather processing. It should be used only in alkaline or neutral solutions (See Formula SH-1, page 122) because in acid solutions, it does not harden. With

CHEMISTRY OF FIXATION

certain individuals, formalin irritates the mucous membranes of the nose and throat and its use is very objectionable.

FORMALIN is a solution of formaldehyde, a gas having a very strong odor. The commercial solution contains 37% of formaldehyde and has the property of hardening gelatin very powerfully, a 5% solution rendering the gelatin of a film insoluble in boiling water in less than a minute.

The characteristics of fixing baths are discussed further under Chapter IX, page 79.

CHAPTER V

THE CHEMISTRY OF WASHING

It may seem strange that a chapter dealing with washing should be inserted in a book on photographic chemistry, because washing is not usually regarded as a chemical operation. Nevertheless, the laws governing washing are distinctly chemical in their nature, and the importance of washing in photography justifies greater attention than is usually paid to the subject.

The object in washing negatives or prints is to remove the chemicals present after the fixing operation. These are principally sodium or ammonium thiosulfate, hardening salts, and complex sodium (or ammonium) thiosulfates. It is known that a fixing bath upon exhaustion accumulates complex silver thiosulfates and that these complex salts are not as easily washed from the material as ordinary hypo. It is, therefore, very important that fixing be as complete as possible to insure the most satisfactory washing.

The best way of insuring complete fixation is to use two fixing baths, and to transfer the negatives or prints to the second bath after they have been fixed in the first. Then, when the first bath begins to show signs of exhaustion and refuses to fix quickly, it should be replaced by a fresh bath. Every other time the first bath is replaced by a fresh bath, the second bath should also be replaced by a fresh bath.

In the case of unhardened films and plates, the mechanism of washing is relatively simple, but, with hardened emulsions some hypo is held by the small quantity of aluminum or chromium hardening compounds retained by the gelatin. A longer washing time will usually remove this small quantity of hypo. With paper prints, however, the paper fibers and baryta coating tenaciously hold some hypo which usually cannot be entirely removed by washing.

The following remarks apply, therefore, to the removal of free hypo other than the traces of retained hypo as mentioned above.

The rate of washing depends largely upon the rate of diffusion of the hypo out of the film into the water providing the water in contact with the film is continuously removed. This diffusion rate has nothing to do with solubility. The solubility of a substance determines the proportion of the substance which can go into solution.

The effect of temperature on the rate of removal of hypo from films and plates is relatively slight but, in any case, it is inadvisable to work at temperatures above 75° F. (24° C.) unless hardening has been accomplished with suitable hardening agents.

Photographic papers, however, wash more slowly in cold water than in warm water because the fixing bath tends to be retained by the paper support as well as the gelatin layer whereas with films and plates the fixing bath is retained only in the gelatin layer. It is important, therefore, that papers be washed thoroughly with water at the correct temperature. Whenever possible, the temperature should be maintained between 65° and 75° F. (18° and 24° C.). If the temperature falls below 65° F. (18° C.) the washing time should be increased. It is not recommended to use wash water for papers at a temperature above 80° F. (27° C.) otherwise troubles from swelling and softening will occur.

The actual rate of washing may be understood by remembering that the quantity of hypo remaining in the gelatin is continually halved in the same period of time as the washing proceeds. An average negative, for instance, will give up half its hypo in fifteen seconds when washed directly under the faucet, so that at the end of fifteen seconds half the hypo will be remaining in it, after thirty seconds one-quarter, after forty-five seconds one-eighth, after one minute one-sixteenth, and so on. It will be seen that in a short time the quantity of hypo remaining will be infinitesimal. This, however, assumes that the negative is continually exposed to fresh water, which is the most important matter in arranging the washing of either negatives or prints.

In most trays and washing tanks an average negative will give up half its hypo in 30 seconds. With a small washing vessel, the process will then tend to stop unless the water is changed. The rate of washing thus turns out to be dependent firstly, on the degree of agitation, and secondly, on the rate of removal of the hypo laden water. This rate is dependent directly on the ratio of the stream of water falling into the vessel and the size of the vessel, quickest renewal taking place when the vessel is small and the stream large. For any given washing vessel, 10 or 12 complete changes of water should occur every hour. The time it requires to change the water in any washing vessel may be determined as follows: While the water is running, an ounce of 1% potassium permanganate solution or red ink is poured into the vessel and the time noted for the water to become completely colorless. If this should require six minutes or less, the rate of flow of water is sufficient.

When the best conditions of agitation and water renewal are used, the following approximate times of washing will effect fairly satisfactory removal of hypo from films, plates, and paper prints:

Lantern Slide Plates	15 to 20 minutes
Film Negatives and Plates, all kinds	30 minutes
Single Weight Papers	60 minutes
Double Weight Papers	1 to 2 hours

If a lot of prints are put in a tray and water allowed to splash on the top of the prints, it is very easy for the water on the top to run off again, and for the prints at the bottom to lie soaking in a pool of fairly strong hypo solution, which is much heavier than water and which will fall to the bottom of the tray. If the quickest washing is desired, washing tanks should be arranged so that the water is changed continuously and completely and the prints or negatives are subjected to a continuous current of fresh water. If water is of value, and it is desired to economize in its use, then by far the most effective way of washing is to use successive changes of small volumes of water, putting the prints first in one tray for two to five minutes, and then transferring them to an entirely fresh lot of water, and repeating this procedure about twelve times.

Since hypo is invisible and its evil effects are not detected till long afterwards, prints or films fresh from the hypo should never be placed among those partly washed. If this is done the entire batch must be washed from the time that the last one was added.

The best way to avoid contamination is to wash in *cascade*. In its simplest form this can be accomplished by placing two trays side by side, one an inch or so above the level of the other. Water is allowed to run into the upper tray and overflow into the lower. All prints and films should be placed in the lower tray before transference to the upper. The operator should also use the lower tray for washing hypo off his fingers.

CHEMISTRY OF WASHING

The prints and films should have at least three minutes preliminary washing before going into the lower washing tray.

The progress of washing can be followed by removing two or three prints or films at intervals from the bath and testing for hypo by using the hypo test formula, directions for which are given on pages 120 and 121.

As a general rule, the hypo will be eliminated adequately from most negative materials in 30 minutes if the rate of flow of water is rapid enough to replace the water in the washing vessel 10 to 12 times per hour. Paper prints should be washed at least one to two hours under these conditions to give a fair degree of freedom from hypo. Prints washed in this manner are usually sufficiently permanent for ordinary purposes when stored in temperate climates. However, when the prints are stored under certain extreme conditions of temperature and humidity (e.g. tropical countries), the quantity of hypo retained may sulfide the silver image or, in other words, a faded print may be produced.

For greatest permanency, with respect to hypo in paper prints, the following procedure should be followed: (1) After fixing in the normal way, the prints should be placed in a fresh fixing bath for 5 minutes and then washed for 30 minutes. (2) The washed prints must then be treated in such a manner as to destroy the last traces of hypo adhering to the paper fibers and baryta coating. Experiments have shown that this residual hypo can be eliminated by treating with an alkaline hydrogen peroxide solution. The presence of hypo may be detected by bathing in a one per cent silver nitrate solution, when a yellowish stain indicates hypo. Details of this procedure are given on page 121. For complete details, see the original paper, "The Elimination of Hypo from Photographic Images," by J. I. Crabtree, G. T. Eaton, and L. E. Muehler, J. Phot. Soc. Amer. 6: p. 6 Nov. 1940.

CHAPTER VI.

THE CHEMISTRY OF REDUCTION AND INTENSIFICATION

Reduction

By reduction in photography is meant the removal of some silver from the image so as to produce a less intense image. Thus, in the case of an over-developed film or plate there will be too much density and contrast, which may be corrected by reducing the negative. In the case of an over-exposed negative there may not be an excess of contrast but the negative will be too dense all over, and in this case what is required is the removal of the excess density.

It is unfortunate that the word "reduction" is used in English for this process. In other languages the word "weakening" is used, and this is undoubtedly a better word, because the chemical action involved in the removal of silver from a negative is oxidation, and the use of the word reduction leads to confusion with true chemical reduction, such as occurs in development.

All the photographic reducers are oxidizing agents, and almost any strong oxidizing agent will act as a photographic reducer and will remove silver, but various oxidizing agents behave differently in respect to the highlights and shadows of the image. Reducing solutions can be classified in three classes:

    A. Subtractive or cutting reducers
        For over-exposed negatives.
    B. Proportional or true scale reducers
        For over-developed negatives.
    C. Super-proportional reducers.
        For over-developed negatives of contrasty subjects.

A. THE SUBTRACTIVE REDUCERS remove an equal quantity of silver from all parts of the image, and consequently remove a larger proportion of the image from the shadows than from the highlights of the negative. The typical subtractive reducer is that known as *Farmer's Reducer,* consisting of a mixture of potassium ferricyanide and hypo, the potassium ferricyanide oxidizing the silver to silver ferrocyanide and the hypo dissolving the latter compound. Farmer's Reducer will not keep when mixed, decomposing rapidly, so that it is usually prepared by making a strong solution of the ferricyanide and then adding a few drops of this to a hypo solution when the reducer is required. It is especially useful for clearing negatives or lantern slides which show slight fog, and is also used for local reduction, the solution being applied with a brush or a wad of absorbent cotton. (See Formula R-4, page 123.)

Another subtractive reducer is permanganate. The permanganates are very strong oxidizing agents, and if a solution of permanganate containing sulfuric acid is applied to a negative, it will oxidize the silver to silver sulfate, which is sufficiently soluble in water to be dissolved. (See Formula R-2, page 122.)

Permanganate has only a very weak action on a negative if no acid is present and this may be made use of for the removal of "dichroic" fog, the yellow or pink stain sometimes produced in development. Dichroic fog consists of very finely divided silver and this is attacked by a solution of plain permanganate (about 0.25%) which will have no appreciable action on the silver of the image.

An important difference should be noted between the behavior of ferricyanide and permanganate when used for reducing pyro-developed negatives. In a negative developed with pyro the image consists partly of the oxidation product of the pyro associated with the silver. (See page 25). When such a negative is reduced with ferricyanide the silver is removed but the stain is unattacked so that the negative appears to become yellower during reduction, though the ferricyanide does not really produce the color, only making it evident by removal of the silver. Permanganate, on the other hand, attacks the stain image in preference to the silver and consequently makes the negative less yellow. Permanganate can also be used as an alternative to ferricyanide for bleaching negatives, since if bromide be added to the solution, silver bromide will be formed and the same bleaching action obtained as with ferricyanide.

POTASSIUM PERMANGANATE occurs in dark purple crystals which dissolve to form a purple solution. It is easily obtained pure but there is a good deal of impure permanganate on the market. Eastman Tested Permanganate is a pure product consisting of very fine crystals which dissolve readily.

In addition to its use for reduction and bleaching, permanganate is employed as a test for hypo, since it is at once reduced by hypo, and the colored solution of the permanganate, therefore, loses its color in the presence of any hypo.

This change is a fair indication of the thoroughness of the elimination of hypo from negatives or prints in washing. When permanganate is reduced in the absence of an excess of free acid, a brownish precipitate of manganese dioxide is obtained and sometimes negatives or prints which have been treated with permanganate are stained brown by this material. Fortunately, manganese dioxide is removed by bisulfite, which reduces it still further, forming a soluble manganese salt. The brown stain can, therefore, be removed by immersion of the stained material in a solution of bisulfite.

A very powerful subtractive reducer is made from a solution of iodine in potassium iodide, to which potassium cyanide has been added to dissolve the silver iodide formed during reduction. Iodine is not soluble in water but is soluble in a solution of potassium iodide. To make up a reducer, dissolve 5 parts of iodine crystals in 100 parts of a 10% solution of potassium iodide. Then dissolve one part of sodium or potassium cyanide in 10 parts of the iodine-iodide solution and make up to 100 parts with water. This solution may be used for reducing either bromide prints or negatives. The activity of the reducer may be decreased by diluting with water.

Warning: Cyanide is a deadly poison and should only be handled in a well ventilated room. Solutions containing cyanide should never be discarded in a sink containing acid, otherwise poisonous hydrogen cyanide gas will be formed. The sink should be well washed out with water after discarding the cyanide solution.

Certain reducers may be classified as falling between pure subtractive and proportional reducers. With these solutions, contrast is decreased as image density is removed from the high and low densities, since a greater proportion of silver is removed from the low densities. A modification of the formula originally suggested by Belitski is of this type, and contains a mixture of ferric chloride (oxidizing agent), hypo, sodium sulfite, potassium citrate and citric acid. An advantage of this solution is that it may be kept 3 to 5 days in a tank, before it needs to be discarded. (See Formula R-8, page 126.)

Farmer's Reducer may also be used to give almost proportional reduction by treating the negative in the ferricyanide solution first, and subsequently in the hypo solution. (See Formula R-4b, page 124.) This method corrects for over-development, whereas the single solution Farmer's Reducer gives only cutting reduction and corrects for over-exposure.

B. Proportional Reducers are those which act on all parts of the negative in proportion to the quantity of silver present there; hence they exactly undo the action of development, since during development the density of all parts of the negative increases proportionally. A correctly exposed but over-developed negative should be reduced with a proportional reducer. Unfortunately, there are no single substances which form exactly proportional reducers, but by mixing permanganate, which is a slightly cutting reducer, with persulfate, which is a super-proportional reducer, a proportional reducer may be obtained. (See Formula R-5, page 125.)

Nearly proportional reduction may be obtained with dilute acidified solutions of ferric alum (ferric ammonium sulfate, although care must be taken to fix and wash the negative thoroughly, to harden it in alkaline formalin before treatment, and to avoid exposing it excessively to the air during treatment in the reducer. (See Formula R-7, page 125.)

C. Super-proportional Reducers are those which act very much more on the heavy deposits than on the light deposits of the negative, and which will consequently reduce the highlights without affecting the detail in the shadows. Only one such reducer is known, and this is ammonium persulfate. Ammonium persulfate is a powerful oxidizing agent and attacks the silver of the negative, transforming it into silver sulfate, which dissolves in the solution. It must be used in an acid solution and is somewhat uncertain in its behavior, occasionally refusing to act, and always acting more rapidly as the reduction progresses. (See Formula R-1, page 126.)

AMMONIUM PERSULFATE is a white crystalline salt, stable when dry. It has been found in the Kodak Research Laboratories that the action of persulfate depends largely upon its containing a very small quantity of iron salt as an impurity, and that its capricious behavior is due to variations in the quantity of iron present. The persulfate supplied as an Eastman Tested Chemical may be relied upon to give a uniform action in reduction.

Intensification

Intensification is photographically the opposite of reduction, the object being to increase contrast. This is done by the deposition of some material on the silver image. A silver image, for instance, can be very much intensified by toning it with uranium (see page 45), the reddish-brown uranium ferrocyanide having very great printing strength and converting a weak negative into one having a great effective contrast for printing purposes. Usually, however, intensification is performed by depositing a silver, mercury or a chromium compound upon the image, and many photographic intensifiers depend upon the use of mercury. But experience has shown that mercury intensified images are not as stable as images produced by chromium intensification.

A useful silver intensifier may be prepared by adding a reducing agent such as Elon to an acid solution of silver nitrate. When a silver image is placed in such a solution, the silver particles (which are being precipitated in the solution) tend to deposit preferentially on the silver grains of the image. The density of the image is thereby increased proportionately. This process, especially for motion picture work, has the advantage that it gives neutral gray (uncolored) images whereas nearly all intensifiers yield a colored image. Also, since the intensified image consists of metallic silver, it is probable that it is as permanent as the original silver image. (See Formula In-5, page 128.)

Mercury is a metal which forms two series of salts, the mercurous salts and the mercuric salts. The latter are in a higher degree of oxidation.

Many of the mercuric salts are insoluble in water, but mercuric chloride is sufficiently soluble for practical use, and when a silver image is placed in a solution of mercuric chloride, this reacts with the silver and forms a mixture of mercurous chloride and silver chloride.

The bleached image, which appears white, can then be treated in various ways. If it is developed, for instance, both the silver chloride and the mercurous chloride will be reduced to the metal, and in addition to the silver, with which we started, we shall have added to every part of silver an equal part of mercury. Instead of using a developer we may blacken the image with ammonia, which forms a black mercury ammonium chloride and produces a high degree of intensification. (See Formula In-1, pages 126 and 127.)

MERCURIC CHLORIDE or Mercury Bichloride, (also commonly known as corrosive sublimate) is a very poisonous salt which should be handled with the utmost care. Its chief use in photography is for intensification. It is ordinarily obtained in white, heavy crystals which are soluble with some difficulty in water.

A very powerful method of intensification, used chiefly for negatives made by photo-engravers, is obtained by bleaching with mercuric chloride and blackening with silver dissolved in potassium cyanide. The use of the cyanide cuts the shadows very slightly at the same time that the highlights are intensified, so that a great increase in the contrast of the negative is obtained. This is usually known as *"Monckhoven's Intensifier."* (See Formula In-1, pages 126 and 127.)

In the case of the chromium intensifier the silver image is bleached with a solution of bichromate containing a very little hydrochloric acid, bichromate being an oxidizer of the same type as permanganate or ferricyanide. The image is then redeveloped and will be found to be intensified to an appreciable extent. This intensifier has found increasing favor owing to the ease and certainty of its operation and the permanency of the intensified image. (See Formula In-4, page 127.)

Warning: Developers containing a high concentration of sulfite, such as D-76 are not suitable for redevelopment, since the sulfite tends to dissolve the bleached image before the developing agents have time to act on it.

POTASSIUM BICHROMATE is made by the oxidation of chromium salts. It forms orange-red crystals, stable in air, and easily dissolves, yielding a yellow solution. It is obtained in a pure form by crystallization. Potassium bichromate is used in photography both for bleaching negatives and for sensitizing gelatin, fish glue, etc. When gelatin containing bichromate is exposed to light it becomes insoluble in water and in this way images may be obtained in insoluble gelatin.

A convenient form of Chromium Intensifier has been placed on the market known as Eastman Chromium Intensifier. It consists of a chemical combination of hydrochloric acid and potassium bichromate, which eliminates the use of liquid hydrochloric acid.

Important: Most reduction or intensification treatments tend to soften the negative and make it more susceptible to scratches. Pre-treatment in an alkaline formalin solution is strongly recommended for all negatives that are to be reduced or intensified. (See Formula SH-1, page 122.)

CHAPTER VII

THE CHEMISTRY OF TONING

The operation of toning consists in the deposition on the silver image of another substance having a different color, in order to get a more pleasing result, or of the transformation of the silver image into another substance for the same purpose.

There are four principal methods of toning:

A. Toning by the replacement of the silver by other metals;
B. Toning by the deposition of salts of metals;
C. Toning by the transformation of the silver image into some substance to which dyes will attach themselves in an insoluble form;
D. Transformation of the silver image into a stable, strongly colored salt of silver.

A. In the case of prints which are made by the printing-out processes, the silver compound produced by the action of light is colored, and after fixation the image left is usually of an unpleasant color, a yellow or yellow-brown. In order to change this to a more satisfactory color it is toned by means of gold or, more rarely, platinum.

When a finely divided silver image is placed in a solution of gold or platinum the silver will replace the metal in solution, going into solution itself, and the gold or platinum will be deposited in the place of the silver. The rate at which these metals are deposited is very important, especially in the case of gold toning. If the gold is deposited too slowly, it will be deposited in a very fine condition, and in the case of finely divided metals, their color depends upon the fineness of the division. Finely divided gold is red, which is not as pleasing as the blue gold obtained by more rapid deposition.

To insure rapid deposition it is necessary that the bath should be kept alkaline, and consequently borax or sodium acetate is added to the gold chloride to make a toning bath, while sometimes substances having a weak reducing action are added, such as sulfocyanides or formates. Platinum toning baths are used in an acid condition.

CHEMISTRY OF TONING

The chemicals used for making up these toning baths must be of high purity, and it is best to get tested chemicals in all cases.

GOLD CHLORIDE is made by dissolving gold in a mixture of hydrochloric and nitric acids and evaporating the solution. It forms brownish crystals, rapidly absorbing water, which contain 65% metallic gold. The salt is sold in small glass tubes containing 15 grains, and in order to use it, the label is removed from the tube and the tube is broken in a bottle containing a known volume of water so that a solution of definite strength is obtained without danger of losing the precious material.

GOLD SODIUM CHLORIDE is a double chloride of gold and sodium which occurs in yellow crystals and contains 49% of metallic gold. It has the advantage over the pure chloride of gold that it is neither acid nor deliquescent.

POTASSIUM CHLOROPLATINITE is the double chloride of platinum and potassium, and is the form in which platinum is used for a toning bath. It occurs in reddish crystals, and is supplied in sealed glass tubes like gold chloride.

LEAD NITRATE and LEAD ACETATE. These colorless salts of lead are sometimes used for toning baths. They are both soluble in water and the solutions are very poisonous.

SODIUM ACETATE, SODIUM PHOSPHATE (Di-basic) and BORAX are all weak alkalis and are used in gold toning baths for this reason. They occur as white salts, soluble in water. Borax occurs as a mineral and is largely used in industry. Only the pure salt should be used for photographic purposes. (See page 24.)

SODIUM THIOCYANATE, SULFOCYANATE, OR SULFOCYANIDE, is a salt occurring in very deliquescent crystals. In order to be at all certain of its strength it must be preserved with great care, out of contact with the air. It is useful as a solvent for silver halides and is also used with gold chloride in toning baths.

B. A good many metallic compounds are colored, and if the silver image is replaced by these colored compounds, wholly or in part, a colored image is obtained. In most of the toning processes based upon the use of colored compounds, ferrocyanides of metals are employed, the silver image being first transformed into silver ferrocyanide, the silver in the silver ferrocyanide being then substituted by another metal of which the ferrocyanide is colored.

The ferro- and ferricyanides are very complex compounds. The cyanides themselves are compounds containing carbon and nitrogen, and have a curious resemblance to chlorides and bromides. Hydrogen unites with carbon and nitrogen to form an acid, HCN, which is called *hydrocyanic acid*, or sometimes prussic acid. The hydrogen in this can be substituted by metals to form cyanides such as potassium cyanide, KCN, which is analogous to potassium chloride, KCl, or potassium bromide, KBr, and on adding a solution of silver nitrate to a soluble cyanide, silver cyanide, AgCN, is precipitated as an insoluble salt, just as silver chloride or silver bromide is precipitated.

There is one respect, however, in which hydrocyanic acid and the cyanides differ from the corresponding chlorine or bromine compounds, and this is that they are extremely poisonous. *A few grains of cyanide swallowed will cause death.*

Cyanide solutions are solvents for the silver halides, forming soluble double compounds with the insoluble silver salts. Potassium cyanide is employed for fixing wet collodion plates, which, being made from silver iodide, are not easily fixed in hypo. Whenever cyanides are used by photographers, their extremely poisonous nature should be remembered and every possible precaution taken in keeping and using them. For example, when discarding a cyanide solution, it should not be poured into a sink or drain where acids are present, otherwise the very poisonous hydrogen cyanide gas will be liberated. A vigorous stream of water should be run into the sink when the cyanide solution is emptied to insure that all traces of the chemical are washed away.

The cyanides easily form complicated double compounds. With sulfur, for instance, they form sulfocyanides, and sodium sulfocyanide has already been referred to as being used in gold toning baths. The cyanides unite with iron cyanides to form two important groups of compounds called *ferrocyanides* and *ferricyanides*. These differ from each other in their degree of oxidation, the ferricyanides being more highly oxidized than the ferrocyanides, so that when a ferricyanide is reduced a ferrocyanide is formed.

POTASSIUM FERROCYANIDE is yellow. It is infrequently known as "yellow prussiate of potash" and has very little application in photography.

POTASSIUM FERRICYANIDE or red prussiate of potash is prepared by passing chlorine gas into a solution of the ferrocyanide and is deposited from concentrated solution as red crystals. Eastman Kodak Company's tested potassium ferricyanide consists of fine red crystals which are readily soluble in water, and give a clear yellow solution.

The value of ferricyanide in photography lies in the fact that ferricyanide oxidizes the silver image and forms silver ferrocyanide from it, so that if a negative is placed in a solution of ferricyanide, it is slowly bleached to silver ferrocyanide.

CHEMISTRY OF TONING

This property can be made use of in various ways. The silver ferrocyanide is soluble in hypo so that if we use a solution of potassium ferricyanide and hypo instead of plain potassium ferricyanide, we shall not get a white image but the silver image will be dissolved slowly, since it will be converted into the silver ferrocyanide by the ferricyanide and then the silver compound formed will be dissolved in the hypo. This mixture of ferricyanide and hypo is known as *Farmer's Reducer*, see Formula R-4, page 123. Again, if we add bromide to our ferricyanide solution, silver bromide is more insoluble than silver ferrocyanide and consequently the silver ferrocyanide as it is produced will be transformed into silver bromide. This operation of transforming a silver image into a bromide image is generally known as *bleaching*. If we combine with the potassium ferricyanide a salt of a metal which gives an insoluble colored ferrocyanide, then we shall get the silver ferrocyanide formed, and this will be converted into the ferrocyanide of the metal whose salt has been added to the bath. If we add an iron salt, such for instance as iron citrate, to the potassium ferricyanide, we shall get a blue iron ferrocyanide formed and the image will be toned blue. If we use uranium nitrate, we shall get the reddish-brown uranium ferrocyanide, while if we use copper citrate, we shall get the red copper ferrocyanide. Sometimes instead of using the metal salt in the same bath as the ferricyanide the operation is done in two steps, the silver being first bleached to silver ferrocyanide, which then combines with a salt of the metal to form the colored metallic ferrocyanide. (See pages 130 to 132.)

C. The range of colors which can be obtained by the use of colored metals or metallic compounds is rather limited, and in order to get a wider range, especially for motion picture and lantern slide work, experimenters have tried to find methods of using dyes and attaching them to the image.

It has been found that this can be done by transforming the silver image into silver iodide, which can be accomplished, for instance, by treatment of the image with a mixture of potassium ferricyanide and potassium iodide. The silver iodide image formed in this way will mordant basic dyes and attach them to the image so that the image assumes the color of the dye. The Kodak Research Laboratories have worked out a process in which instead of transforming the silver image into silver iodide, it is treated with a uranium mordanting bath and transformed into a mixture of uranium and silver ferrocyanides, and then the basic dyes are mordanted onto this image. (See formulas on pages 132 to 135.)

D. Silver sulfide is a very insoluble compound of silver, and consequently if a silver image or a silver halide salt is treated with sulfur or a sulfide respectively they will at once be transformed into silver sulfide. Silver sulfide has a color varying from light brown to black, according to its state of subdivision, and the transformation of the image into silver sulfide is by far the most popular method of toning developing-out paper prints, the prints so toned being generally known as "sepia" prints.

When great permanency is required prints should preferably be toned to a silver sulfide image since experience has shown that this form of silver is one of the most stable. There are two general methods of transforming the image into silver sulfide:

1. Direct toning, with the hypo alum bath; and
2. Bleaching and redevelopment.

1. As was explained in the chapter dealing with fixing, when an acid is added to a solution of hypo, it tends to precipitate sulfur. Now, a solution of alum in water is weakly acid, so that if alum is added to plain hypo without any sulfite present, the solution will, after a time, become turbid and precipitate sulfur. This solution of alum and hypo at the point where it is ready to precipitate the sulfur may be considered as having free sulfur in solution, and if prints are immersed in a hot solution of alum and hypo (about 120° F.) (49° C.), the silver image will be converted directly into silver sulfide and the prints will be toned brown. Two precautions are necessary in order to obtain successful results with the hypo-alum toning bath. The bath works best at a temperature of 120° F. (49° C.); if the temperature is allowed to rise much above 120° F. (49° C.) there is danger of blistering and bleaching of the image. A fresh bath tends to weaken the print, eating out the highlights. To prevent this a little silver must be added to the bath preferably in the form of silver chloride as given under the hypo-alum toning bath Formula T-1a, page 137. A bath lasts for a long time, and as a general rule a hypo-alum bath which has been somewhat used works better than a fresh bath. The color of the final tone is related directly to the color of the original black-and-white image. Blue-black images give cold chocolate tones; olive green images give warm sepia tones.

CHEMISTRY OF TONING

When gold chloride is added to a slightly alkaline hypo alum bath, it is possible to remove the prints at any stage of the toning operation and obtain prints which vary in tone from a warm black through to a reddish brown, depending on the time of toning. With the usual hypo alum bath, toning must be carried to completion before removing the print in order to avoid the tendency of the bath to tone the highlights faster than the shadows (double tones). The usual gold toning bath can be used only a few times before it begins to give poor tones and should be discarded. A modified formula, called the Nelson Gold Toning Bath (Formula T-21, page 139) containing ammonium persulfate does not give double tones and can be used repeatedly when revived by additions of gold chloride. The persulfate undoubtedly causes a slight etching of the silver image and facilitates the interaction of the silver grains with the gold chloride.

2. It is rather troublesome to use a bath which has to be heated, so that while hypo-alum toning is used on the large scale, smaller quantities of prints are commonly toned by bleaching the silver print in a bath of ferricyanide and bromide, and then treating the bleached print after washing, with sodium sulfide, which converts the silver bromide directly into silver sulfide. This process is quite satisfactory for use with amateur prints and enlargements.

SODIUM SULFIDE occurs as white transparent crystals which have a strong affinity for water. The crystals absorb oxygen rapidly unless they are carefully protected from the air. By melting the crystals and driving off all of the water, fused sodium sulfide is obtained containing no moisture and of more definite purity. One part by weight of the fused sulfide is equivalent to three parts by weight, approximately, of the crystals.

The impurity chiefly found in fused sodium sulfide is iron, in the form of iron sulfide, which can be removed by dissolving the sodium sulfide in hot water and allowing the iron sulfide to separate out as a black sludge, leaving a clear, colorless solution which can be decanted off. Eastman Kodak Company's tested Sodium Sulfide, fused, contains a minimum of iron sulfide. Old sodium sulfide which has been kept improperly, such as in loosely corked bottles, often contains hypo, and if this is present in any considerable quantity some of the silver bromide will be dissolved by the hypo, and the print will lose strength in the highlights and give an inferior result.

All sulfides give off a certain quantity of hydrogen sulfide, which smells offensively, and which is extremely dangerous to unexposed photographic materials, since a very small quantity of hydrogen sulfide will convert enough of the silver bromide or chloride of the material into sulfide to produce a severe fog. No photographic materials should therefore be stored in a room where sulfides are kept or where sulfide toning is done.

It has already been explained that the color of silver sulfide depends upon its state of division, and since the state of division of the toned image depends upon that of the untoned image and this again upon the treatment of the material, it is evident that the exposure and development of the print will have an effect upon the result obtained. As a general rule, it may be stated that to get good colors in sulfide toning it is necessary that a print should have been fully developed but not over-exposed. If a trace of iron is present in the ferricyanide-bromide solution used as the bleach in the redevelopment process, for example, from a defective enameled tray, blue spots composed of ferric ferrocyanide are liable to form. This tendency to form spots is reduced to a minimum by adding potassium oxalate to the bleach bath since the blue iron salt is soluble in the oxalate. Acetic acid is added also, to prevent possible formation of blisters (see Formula T-7a, page 138).

CHAPTER VIII

PREPARING SOLUTIONS

A solution of any kind is obtained by dissolving a solid, a liquid or a gas in another liquid (or solid). The substance being dissolved is called the *solute* and the liquid in which it is dissolved is called the *solvent*. The extent to which the solute is soluble in the solvent is called its solubility and when the solvent will hold no more of the solute it is said to be saturated.

The degree of solubility of any chemical depends on the nature of the solvent and on the temperature, which should always be stated.

If a saturated solution is cooled to a lower temperature, crystals usually form which settle out until the saturation point is reached at that particular temperature, though in the case of a substance like hypo, if all dust is excluded, crystals do not separate out on cooling and a so-called super-saturated solution is obtained. However, if a small crystal of hypo is added to the solution, crystals immediately form and continue to grow until the saturation point is reached. The best method of preparing a saturated solution, therefore, is to dissolve the chemical in hot water, cool to room temperature with shaking, allow to stand, and filter.

For photographic work, saturated solutions are not recommended because of their unreliability relative to the concentration of the chemicals used. Solutions of definite percentage strength are to be preferred and are always specified in Eastman formulas.

When a chemical is dissolved in water the volume of the solution is usually greater than that of the water, because the particles or molecules of the chemical occupy a certain space when in solution. In case two liquids are mixed, the final volume of the liquid is not necessarily equal to the sum of the volumes of the liquids mixed; it may be greater or it may be less. Thus fifty volumes of alcohol when added to fifty volumes of water at 70° F., produce ninety-seven volumes of the mixture and not one hundred. Moreover, equal weights of different chemicals do not occupy the same volume.

In photography we are concerned only with the weight or volume of each chemical in a fixed volume of the solution, so

50 ELEMENTARY PHOTOGRAPHIC CHEMISTRY

that when mixing, the chemical should be dissolved in a volume of water appreciably less than that called for in the formula and then water added *up to* the volume stated.

When mixing photographic solutions, the importance of following manufacturers' instructions issued with formulas cannot be over estimated. The quantities and the order of ingredients have been established by extensive tests and to change them is very apt to affect the useful properties of the solutions.

Weights and Measures

In photographic practice, solids are weighed and liquids are measured either by the Avoirdupois or the Metric system.

The following tables of weights and measures give all the equivalent values required for converting photographic formulas:

Weights and Measures—Conversion Tables*

Avoirdupois to Metric Weight

Pounds	Ounces	Grains	Grams	Kilograms
1	16	7000	453.6	0.4536
0.0625	1	437.5	28.35	0.02835
		1	0.0648	
	0.03527	15.43	1	0.001
2.205	35.27	15430	1000	1

U. S. Liquid to Metric Measure

Gallons	Quarts	Ounces (Fluid)	Drams (Fluid)	Cubic Centimeters	Liters
1	4	128	1024	3785	3.785
0.25	1	32	256	946.3	0.9463
		1	8	29.57	0.02957
0.000975	0.0039	0.125	1 (60 mins.)	3.697	0.003697
		0.03381	0.2705	1	0.001
0.2642	1.057	33.81	270.5	1000	1

Solid Conversion Values

Grains per 32 ozs. multiplied by 0.06847 = grams per liter
Ounces per 32 ozs. multiplied by 29.96 = grams per liter
Pounds per 32 ozs. multiplied by 479.3 = grams per liter

Grams per liter multiplied by 14.60 = grains per 32 ozs.
Grams per liter multiplied by 0.03338 = ounces per 32 ozs.
Grams per liter multiplied by 0.002086 = pounds per 32 ozs.

Liquid Conversion Values
(U. S. System)

Ounces (fluid) per 32 ozs. multiplied by 31.25 = cubic centimeters per liter.
Cubic centimeters per liter multiplied by 0.032 = ounces (fluid) per 32 ozs.

*These tables do not apply when converting British Imperial to metric measure

PREPARING SOLUTIONS

When a formula is expressed in grains, ounces, and pounds, it may be converted into a metric formula by using the conversion values on page 50 which take into account the difference between 32 ounces and one liter. After a conversion has been made, the values obtained should be rounded off to give convenient working quantities. The error introduced in rounding off a value should not be greater than 3 per cent and the ratio between chemicals such as Elon and hydroquinone, or carbonate and sulfite should not be changed.

Thus a developer formula for a 42 gallon tank would be converted as follows:

Formula

Water	5 gallons
Elon	1 ounce 25 grains
Sodium Sulfite, desiccated	52 ounces
Potassium Metabisulfite	1 ounce 272 grains
Hydroquinone	4 ounces 86 grains
Pyro	10 ounces
Sodium Carbonate, desiccated	27 ounces 358 grains
Potassium Bromide	260 grains
Add water to make	42 gallons

Conversion

	Direct	Rounded-off
Water	20.0 liters	20 liters
Elon	31.7 grams	32 grams
Sodium Sulfite, desiccated	1557.9 grams	1560 grams
Potassium Metabisulfite	48.6 grams	49 grams
Hydroquinone	125.7 grams	126 grams
Pyro	299.6 grams	300 grams
Sodium Carbonate, desiccated	833.3 grams	835 grams
Potassium Bromide	17.8 grams	18 grams
Add water to make	168.0 liters	168 liters

To convert a metric formula into an avoirdupois formula, the process should be reversed using the values given in the second part of the foregoing conversion table. Values in grains should be rounded off to the nearest quarter ounce, whenever it is possible to do so without introducing an error greater than 3 per cent.

It is often recommended to dissolve, say, 10 parts of a solid in 100 parts of water. In the case of liquids, parts should be taken as meaning units of volume and in the case of solids as units of weight. A "part" may, therefore, mean anything from a grain to a ton, or a minim to a gallon so long as the other quantities are reckoned in the same units of weight or volume. (OVER)

Thus:

For use, take		For use, take
Solution A...... 3 parts	may mean	Solution A...... 15 ozs.
Solution B...... 1 part		Solution B...... 5 ozs.

If the formula contains both solids and liquids, if ounces (liquid) and ounces (solid) are substituted for "parts," the error involved falls within permissible limits.

Example:

Mix one gallon of solution according to the following formula:

Sodium Sulfite	10 parts
Pyro	1 part
Water to make	100 parts

One gallon equals 128 ozs. Therefore, dissolve $10 \times 128 \div 100 = 12\ 4/5$ ozs. of sulfite in water, add $1\frac{1}{4}$ ozs. of Pyro, and make up to one gallon.

When quantities of chemicals under 10 grains or 0.7 gram are included in a formula, they are expressed preferably as a 10 per cent solution to be added as so many drams or cc. If less than a dram is required, an even quarter fraction thereof ought to be used. This plan avoids expressing the volume in "drops," which is a very uncertain quantity varying as much as 150 per cent depending on the way it is measured and the specific gravity of the liquid used. The average drop from the usual dropping bottle or burette measures about one minim or about one twentieth of a cc.

Many photographers are accustomed to making up their stock solutions of hypo, carbonate, sulfite, etc., by means of the hydrometer. This method has the advantage that in case the chemical has become moist and contains an unknown quantity of water, a definite reading on the hydrometer will give a solution of the same strength as if perfectly dry chemicals had been used. When a stock solution is made from moist chemicals by weighing, the error caused by the presence of water may be as high as 25% or 50%.

The hydrometer method has the disadvantage that the adjustment of a solution to the required strength takes considerable time, the hydrometer reading does not convey any idea as to the percentage strength of the solution, and the reading varies with the temperature. For instance, if a stock solution is made with hot water and this registers, say, 45° Baumé (Bé.) on the hydrometer, on cooling, the liquid may register 48° or 50° Bé. It is therefore absolutely necessary

PREPARING SOLUTIONS

either to make all readings when the solutions have cooled to room temperature, or to prepare a table giving the variation of density of each solution with temperature.

For example, the specific gravity of acetic acid with increasing concentration of acid at 59°F. (15°C.) increases to a maximum of 1.07 at 80% and then decreases to 1.058 at 99% acid.

A hydrometer is useful, however, in checking the strength of certain liquid chemicals, such as alcohol, hydrochloric acid, and sulfuric acid. If a solution is known to contain only pure ethyl alcohol and water, for example, then from the hydrometer reading at a definite temperature the percentage strength can be determined with accuracy.

Mixing stock solutions by hydrometer test is not recommended because it is much simpler to compound these by weighing. A subsequent hydrometer reading, however, is sometimes a rough check that the solution has been mixed correctly. *A hydrometer test of a mixed developer or fixing bath has no meaning whatever for determining its state of exhaustion.* The only way to test a photographic solution is actually to process therein the photographic material for which it was intended.

Stock Solutions

A stock solution is a concentrated solution to which water is added before use.

The limiting strength of solution which it is possible to make in any particular case depends on the solubility of the chemical, and as the solubility diminishes with temperature, a solution should not be made stronger than a saturated solution at 40°F.,(4.4°C) otherwise, in cold weather, the substance would crystallize out. (See Table of Solubilities, page 156.)

A stock solution of sodium sulfite should be made as strong as possible (20% of the desiccated salt) because at such a strength the solution oxidizes very slowly and will therefore keep, whereas in weaker solution, it combines with the oxygen in the air very readily and is then useless as a preservative.

Percentage Solutions

The percentage strength of a photographic solution indicates the quantity of the chemical which is dissolved in 100 ounces or 100 cc. of the solution. A percentage solution is prepared by dissolving the specified quantity of the chemical in a small volume of water and adding water to make 100 ounces (or 100 cc.). In the avoirdupois system a 10% solution of a solid is made by taking one ounce and making up to 10 ounces with water. Converting these figures into grams and cc. we have, roughly, 30 grams in 300 cc. or a 10% solution.

A 10% solution of a liquid in water is made by taking 10 ounces or 10 cc. of the liquid and adding water to make 100 ounces or 100 cc. respectively.

The great advantage of stating the strength of any solution in parts per hundred is that a definite mental picture is at once created of its relative strength, while by means of a number of stock solutions it is possible to compound certain formulas by simply measuring out a definite volume of each solution thus dispensing with a balance. Thus supposing we have 10% solutions of potassium ferricyanide and of potassium bromide already at hand and it is desired to make up the following solution:

Potassium Ferricyanide	6.0 grams
Potassium Bromide	2.3 grams
Water to make	1000.0 cc.

then it is only necessary to measure out 60 cc. of the ferricyanide solution, 23 cc. of the bromide solution, and add water to make 1000 cc.

Suppose a formula calls for 0.1 gram. It is impossible to weigh this quantity accurately on the usual photographic scale, but by measuring out 10 cc. of a 1% solution, and adding this to the mixture the problem is solved.

Terminology and Arrangement of Formulas

In the publication of formulas it is convenient from several standpoints to adopt a standard volume of solution for tray and tank work. Eastman formulas are published, therefore, on a 32 ounce or one liter basis or quarter fraction thereof for tray purposes, and a one gallon or one liter or quarter fraction thereof for tank purposes. For special purposes such as motion picture or photo finishing work it is customary to publish larger avoirdupois volumes for deep tank formulas.

As a general rule in published formulas the term "Cold water to make" is always given at the end of the formula. This insures dilution to a definite volume, thus yielding a known concentration of chemicals each time the formula is mixed. With many developers a volume of water at about 125° F. (52° C.) is given at the beginning of the formula, sufficient to dissolve all the chemicals. When finally diluted to volume with cold water, the solution will usually be at a satisfactory working temperature, 65° to 70° F. (18° to 21°C.).

The term "Stock Solution" should precede every formula which needs to be diluted for use. As mentioned previously, the order of chemicals in a formula is established carefully and should always be followed when preparing a solution.

Names of chemicals used in Eastman formulas are those accepted by standard text books of chemistry. Vague or inaccurate terms such as sulfuret of hydrogen, soda crystals, liver of sulfur, etc., are eliminated.

Apparatus

For quantities up to 4 pounds or 2000 grams a double pan balance should be used. For still larger quantities a platform scale may be used. For preparing very dilute solutions of dyes, desensitizers, or developers, a small chemical balance weighing to one-tenth of a grain or one-hundredth gram is necessary.

For small volumes of solution conical glass flasks are the most suitable, for larger volumes enameled or hard rubber buckets. Earthenware crocks are usually unsatisfactory because when the glaze cracks, the solutions penetrate the pores and thus contaminate any other solutions subsequently mixed in them.

A wooden stick or paddle made of spruce or cypress is the best form of stirrer, but a separate one should be used for each solution to eliminate the possibility of contamination. Hard rubber stirring rods are satisfactory for use with small volumes of solution. For mixing larger volumes (2 to 20 gallons) (8 to 80 liters), a useful mixing device consists of a metal rod (inconel, nickel, or 18-8 stainless steel*) with a flat metal disc fastened to one end. For still larger volumes, portable automatic stirrers are entirely satisfactory, if constructed of inconel or 18-8 Mo stainless steel*.

Definite volumes for different mixing vessels are best indicated by making lines on the inside of the vessel for each volume.

Materials for making containers for photographic solutions vary according to the nature and volume of the solutions to be used. Trays and small tanks are usually satisfactory if made from any of the following: glass, (such as

*Stainless steels (18% chromium—8% nickel and containing small percentages of other metals) are supplied by several manufacturers in the United States under various trade names, such as Allegheny Metal, Carpalloy 8, Enduro KA-2, Rezistal KA-2, U. S. S. 18-8, etc. Mo = Molybdenum.

Pyrex) enameled steel, reinforced hard rubber, wax impregnated wood (cypress or spruce), wood lined with a good grade of sheet rubber or rubberized cloth, well glazed porcelain, or laminated phenolic condensation products.

Small tanks with welded seams and trays pressed from 18-8 stainless steel containing 2 to 4% molybdenum (Mo) appear promising, provided they are used with developers, rinse baths, fixing baths, and wash water only. Thermoplastic rubber compounds (sulfur-free) are satisfactory for construction of trays and small tanks.

Large tanks, vats, and drums should be made of hard glazed stoneware, Alberene stone, wax impregnated spruce or cypress, rubber coated steel, 18-8 Mo stainless steel with welded joints, or wood lined with lead having "burned" seams. Another simple inexpensive method of tank construction is to flow hot asphalt (m.p. 250° to 300° F.) over the surface of a cypress wood tank. Wood, stoneware, or metal surfaces treated with several coats of Kodacoat paint are protected satisfactorily from the corrosive attack of photographic solutions in common use.

Tin, copper, and zinc, or alloys of these metals will usually produce bad fog and stain with photographic developers, and are also unsatisfactory for use in fixing baths.

Mixing Operations

Chemicals should be weighed and solutions prepared outside the darkroom. Care must be taken when handling such substances as hydroquinone, resublimed pyro, potassium ferricyanide, etc., not to shake the finer particles into the air, otherwise they will enter the ventilating system and settle on benches, negatives and prints, thus causing no end of trouble in the way of spots and stains.

Weigh chemicals on pieces of paper and after transferring to the mixing vessel do not shake the paper but lay it in the sink and allow water to flow over it, thus dissolving the dust. Larger quantities are most conveniently weighed in buckets.

For small volumes of solutions a glass graduate marked off in ounces should be used; for larger volumes use a bucket previously graduated, or mark off the inside of the tank or crock used for mixing. When measuring a liquid in a glass graduate, place the eye on a level with the graduation mark and pour in the liquid until its lower surface coincides with this level. Owing to capillary attraction the liquid in contact

PREPARING SOLUTIONS

with the walls of the graduate is drawn up the sides, so that on viewing sideways it appears as though the liquid has two surfaces. All readings should be made from the lower surface and at room temperature because a warm liquid contracts on cooling.

The rapidity with which a substance dissolves in any solvent depends on its solubility and degree of fineness, the nature and temperature of the solvent, and the rate of stirring.

Since most solutions are intended for use at ordinary temperatures (65° to 70° F.) (18° to 21° C.), if hot water is used for dissolving, the solution must be cooled again if it is required for immediate use, though usually the time taken to do this is less than the extra time which would be taken up in dissolving the chemicals in cold water. When mixing, therefore, as a general rule, dissolve the chemical in as small a volume of warm water (about 125° F.) (52° C.) as possible, cool and dilute with cold water.

In some cases it is possible to dissolve all constituents of a formula by using 75 or 80 per cent of the total volume of water at a temperature of 65° to 75° F. (18° to 24° C.). Such a procedure saves cost of heating water as well as the time required to cool the solution when water at 125° F. (52° C.) is used.

After diluting with water, thoroughly shake the solution if in a bottle, or stir if in a tank, otherwise the water added will simply float on top of the heavier solution.

When mixing a solution in a tank, never put the dry chemicals into the tank, but always make sure that they are dissolved by mixing in separate buckets and filtering into the tank.

In the case of dry salts, such as desiccated sodium carbonate and sodium sulfite, *always add the chemical to the water and not vice versa, otherwise a hard cake will form which will dissolve only with difficulty.*

One of the advantages of the alkali, *Kodalk*, is that it does not cake when added to water, regardless of the manner in which it is poured in.

If monohydrated sodium carbonate is used in a formula calling for desiccated carbonate, the quantity of the dry salt must be increased by 17% to allow for the water content of the monohydrated salt.

It is necessary to remove from the solution any suspended matter such as dirt, caused by the presence of dust in the chemicals used, and also any residue or undissolved particles which might settle on the film, plates or paper during development.

The removal of particles remaining in a solution after mixing may be accomplished by any of the following methods:

(a) Allow the solution to stand and draw off or decant the clear supernatant liquid. This method is particularly useful when the suspended matter is so fine that it will pass through a filter.

The settling of a semi-colloidal sludge can usually be hastened by mixing the solution in warm water, because the warmth tends to coagulate the suspension and cause the particles to cluster together. Thus if crystals of sodium sulfide which are brown, due to the presence of iron, are dissolved in warm water the colloidal iron sulfide coagulates and settles out rapidly, leaving a perfectly colorless solution.

(b) For volumes of solution up to five gallons, filter through a fine cloth into a bottle or crock fitted with a side tube about an inch above the bottom. In this way the fine particles settle but the drainage tube is sufficiently high so as not to disturb the sediment. The cloth or muslin should be washed thoroughly, otherwise the sizing matter in the fabric will be washed into the solution and settle as a sludge.

A hard rubber tube and a faucet represent a satisfactory type of outlet for stoneware or 18-8 Mo stainless steel tanks. The hard rubber tube should be inserted through a soft rubber stopper fitted into the hole in the side of the tank or jar.

(c) For large volumes of solutions such as are used in photo finishing work, the best arrangement for mixing is to place the chemical room immediately above the developing room, and to mix the solutions in large wooden vats, stoneware or enameled tanks connected with 18-8 Mo stainless steel, hard rubber, or rubber lined iron piping to the developing and fixing tanks in the darkroom below. The solutions can then be mixed in advance, allowed to settle, and tested, so that only correct solutions pass into the tanks.

When mixing large volumes of solution in a tank, stretch a cloth filter bag over the tank, place the chemicals in the bag and allow hot water to flow into it. In this way the chemicals are dissolved and the solution filtered at the same time. A separate bag should be used for each solution to eliminate all risk of contamination.

Finely divided chemicals should be dissolved separately in enameled pails, using a small volume of warm water (about

125° F.) (52° C.), and then filtered by pouring into filter bag.

When mixing chemicals, if the solution is not filtered or if a coarse filter is used, a scum usually rises to the surface consisting of fibers, dust, etc., which should be skimmed off with a towel.

When a fixing bath has been used for some time and is allowed to stand undisturbed for a few days, any hydrogen sulfide gas which may be present in the atmosphere forms a metallic looking scum of silver sulfide at the surface of the liquid, and on immersing the film this scum attaches itself to the gelatin and prevents the action of the fixing bath. Any such scum should be removed carefully before use, with a sheet of blotting paper or by using a skimmer made of several layers of cheese cloth stretched on a frame.

The Water Supply in Photographic Operations

Water is the most widely used chemical in photography and it is important therefore to know to what extent the impurities in it may be harmful to the various photographic operations and how these impurities may be removed.

Impurities in Water. Excluding distilled water, rain water, and water from clean melted ice or snow, impurities may be present as follows:

1. Dissolved salts such as bicarbonates, chlorides, and sulfates of calcium, magnesium, sodium, and potassium.

2. Suspended matter which may consist of:
   A. Mineral matter such as mud, iron rust, or free sulfur.
   B. Vegetable matter such as decayed vegetation, fungus growths and micro-organisms.

The suspended particles may be of colloidal dimensions when they are difficult to remove by filtration.

3. Dissolved extracts usually colored yellow or brown from decayed vegetable matter and the bark of trees.

4. Dissolved gases such as air, carbon dioxide, and hydrogen sulfide.

Impurities in the water supply are not responsible, however, for as many troubles as is usually supposed. If developing solutions are mixed with warm water (about 125°F.) (52° C.) and allowed to stand over night, any precipitate or suspended matter will settle and the clear supernatant liquid may be drawn off for use. The presence of calcium and other salts is sometimes beneficial as they tend to retard the swelling of the gelatin coating of films, plates, and papers during washing. This is of particular advantage in hot weather.

The only impurities liable to cause serious trouble with developers are hydrogen sulfide or soluble metallic sulfides. With such water about 60 grains of lead acetate per gallon (one gram per liter) of developer should be added before mixing. This removes the sulfides, as lead sulfide and any excess lead is precipitated in the developer and settles on standing.

No trouble may be anticipated with fixing baths prepared with average samples of impure water providing the bath is clarified by settling before use.

When washing photographic materials little trouble may be anticipated with uncolored water if the following precautions are taken: (a) remove all suspended matter by filtering, either by means of commercial filters or by placing two or three layers of cloth over the water outlet; (b) remove thoroughly all excess moisture from the films, plates or paper before drying.

Water which even after filtering is colored brown is very apt to cause staining of the highlights of paper prints. It is a difficult matter to remove economically the coloring matter from such waters and each case usually requires specific treatment.

How to Mix Developing Solutions

A developer usually contains four ingredients as follows:

1. *The developing agent* (Elon, hydroquinone, pyro, para-aminophenol, etc.).

2. *The alkali* (carbonates and hydroxides of sodium, potassium, lithium and ammonium, Kodalk, borax, etc.).

3. *The preservative* (sulfites, bisulfites, and metabisulfites of sodium and potassium).

4. *The restrainer* (bromides and iodides of sodium and potassium).

If a developing agent like hydroquinone is dissolved in water, the solution will either not develop at all or only very slowly, and on standing it will gradually turn brown, because of what is called oxidation or chemical combination of the hydroquinone with the oxygen present in the air in contact with the surface of the liquid. This oxidation product is of the nature of a dye and will stain fabrics or gelatin just like a dye solution.

On adding a solution of an alkali such as sodium carbonate, the hydroquinone at once becomes a developer, but at the same time the rate of oxidation is increased to such an extent that the solution very rapidly turns dark brown, and if a film is developed in this solution it becomes stained and fogged.

If we add a little sodium bisulfite to the brown colored solution mentioned above, the brown color or stain is bleached out and a colorless solution is obtained. Therefore, if the preservative is first added to the developer, on adding the accelerator, the solution should remain perfectly clear because the sulfite preserves or protects the developing agent from oxidation by the air.

As a general rule, therefore, the preservative should be dissolved first.

An exception to this rule should be observed with concentrated formulas containing the developing agent Elon, or a similar developing agent in concentrated solution. This substance is readily soluble in warm water (about 125° F.) (52° C.) and does not oxidize rapidly. If the sulfite is dissolved before the Elon, a white precipitate often appears especially if the sulfite solution is concentrated.

This precipitate forms because Elon is a combination of an insoluble base with an acid which renders it soluble. When the acid portion is neutralized by a weak alkali such as sodium sulfite, the insoluble base is precipitated. This Elon precipitate is soluble in an excess of water and also in a sodium carbonate solution with which the base forms a soluble sodium salt. When once the Elon is dissolved, however, it takes a fairly high concentration of sulfite to bring it out of solution again, though only a low concentration of sulfite is required to prevent the Elon from dissolving. If a precipitate forms on dissolving the Elon and sulfite, this will usually redissolve on adding the carbonate and no harm has been done.

Some direction sheets recommend that a portion of the sulfite should be dissolved in order to prevent the oxidation of the Elon, then dissolve the Elon, and then the remainder of the sulfite. Many workers add a little of the solid sulfite to the Elon when dissolving the latter. This procedure is quite satisfactory, though if the Elon is dissolved alone in water at a temperature not above 125° F. (52° C.), and the sulfite dissolved immediately afterwards, little or no oxidation products will be formed which would otherwise produce chemical stain.

The alkali may be added in one of three ways:

(a) Dissolve the alkali separately and add to the cooled Elon-sulfite solution. There is danger with carbonate, however, of the Elon precipitating before the carbonate is added.

(b) Add the solid alkali to the Elon-sulfite solution, stirring thoroughly until dissolved.

(c) After dissolving the Elon, dissolve the sulfite and alkali together, cool and add to the Elon-solution.

Bromides and iodides are added to a developer to compensate for any chemical fog produced by the developer, or inherent in the emulsion. It is immaterial at what stage they are added during the mixing.

General Hints on Mixing Developers

1. *Water Temperature.* Use water at 125° F. (52° C.) or less except when a higher temperature is specifically recommended.

2. *Containers.* Use good enamelled, glass, or hard rubber. Avoid tin, copper, or galvanized iron which cause fog.

3. *Check the Formulas.* Arrange the chemicals needed for mixing at one end of a shelf or bench. As each one is weighed out, place the stock can or bottle on the opposite side of the shelf or bench. Use only chemicals of reliable manufacture.

4. *Water First.* Pour water into the container, and then add the chemicals. Caking results from adding water to dry chemicals. Boiling water should never be used unless specifically recommended.

5. *Avoid Premature Oxidation.* Add a little sulfite to the water before adding the developing agents. This is not necessary with Elon because of its slow rate of oxidation.

6. *Complete Solution of Each Chemical.* Dissolve each chemical completely before adding the next, and in the order given in the published formula.

Practical Rules for Mixing Developers

The following practical procedures are recommended for mixing developers, unless definite instructions otherwise are given with the formula.

A. For Mixing Less than 5 Gallons of Developer.

PREPARING SOLUTIONS

1. Weigh out all of the chemicals, placing each one on a separate piece of paper on which its name and weight are written. It is then possible to check the chemicals before starting to dissolve them, thus greatly reducing the possibility of error. Be sure that the scales are sufficiently accurate, particularly for the developing agents, potassium bromide, and any other ingredients which are used in small quantities.

2. Into a container large enough to take the full final volume of solution place a volume of warm water (not over 125° F.) (52° C.), equal to one-half to three-quarters of the total volume to be used.

3. If there is Elon in the formula, add it to the water and stir until it is completely dissolved.

4. Add the sulfite or other preservative (bisulfite, potassium metabisulfite, etc.) and stir until fully dissolved.

5. Add the remaining developing agents (hydroquinone, pyro, etc.) and make sure that they are completely dissolved.

6. If the formula contains an acid material, in addition to a carbonate, the acid substance should be dissolved and mixed in with thorough stirring.

7. Dissolve the alkali (carbonate, Kodalk, borax, etc.) and mix. If the formula contains caustic soda, it should be dissolved separately in a small volume of *cold* water. Then pour the caustic solution in slowly while stirring the remainder of the developer.

8. Dissolve the potassium bromide and any other remaining ingredients.

9. After all the chemicals have been dissolved in turn, add sufficient cold water to bring the solution up to the correct volume, and stir thoroughly in order to mix the water with the heavier solutions already present.

10. Filtering is unnecessary if clear water and clean chemicals are used, but if there is evidence of a sediment or suspension, the solution should be filtered before use or storage.

11. If the solution is not to be used immediately, it should be placed in a clean bottle of the proper size, stoppered, and labeled plainly.

An example of this method of mixing is as follows:

(OVER).

Developer A

	Avoirdupois	Metric
Elon	45 grains	3.1 grams
Sodium Sulfite, desiccated	1½ ounces	45.0 grams
Hydroquinone	135 grains	9.5 grams
Sodium Carbonate, desiccated	2½ ounces	75.0 grams
Potassium Bromide	15 grains	1.1 grams
Water to make	32 ounces	1.0 liter

Dissolve the Elon in 16 ounces (500 cc.) of water (about 125° F.) (52° C.), then add the sulfite, and when completely dissolved, add the hydroquinone. Finally add the carbonate and bromide and cold water to make 32 ounces (one liter).

An alternative method to the above consists in weighing out and mixing the dry chemicals. Pour the mixture slowly into 90 per cent of the total volume of water with rapid stirring and then dilute to volume. This method is only satisfactory for small volumes of solution. The dry chemicals must also be mixed uniformly and added immediately to the water. If the dry mixture is allowed to stand around for an hour or so, it may absorb moisture from the air, dissolve with great difficulty, and produce a colored solution.

B. For Mixing Moderately Large Volumes of Developer (5 to 500 Gallons)

The following procedure is safe and is probably more economical of time.

1. Weigh out the chemicals and check all weights carefully. It facilitates weighing if two pairs of scales are provided, a large one for weighing out the carbonate and sulfite, and a small one for weighing developing agents, bromide, etc.

2. In a tank large enough to take the final volume of solution, place a volume of water equal to about one tenth the final volume.

3. In a separate container (enamelled pail or rubber bucket) dissolve each of the chemicals in turn in a small volume of warm water (not over 125° F.) (52° C.) and add to the tank, stirring after each addition to insure thorough mixing. A small quantity of the sulfite solution should be saved and added to the water in which the developing agents are dissolved. With some developing agents, hydroquinone for example, the total quantity should be divided into two or more parts and each part dissolved separately. Also, it is usually desirable to cool the tank solution somewhat by adding a portion of cold water before adding the solution of the alkali.

PREPARING SOLUTIONS

4. Add cold water to bring the solution to the correct volume and stir thoroughly to insure complete mixing of all ingredients.

As an alternative to the above, the filter bag method may be more convenient. In this method, a cloth bag is suspended over the tank and each chemical placed in it and dissolved in turn by allowing a stream of warm water to flow through the bag into the tank. Do not add the water so rapidly that the final volume is reached before all the chemicals are dissolved.

An example of this second method of mixing is as follows:

Developer B

	Avoirdupois	Metric
Sodium Sulfite, desiccated	4 pounds	1800.0 grams
Hydroquinone	13 ounces	390.0 grams
Sodium Carbonate, desiccated	4 pounds	1800.0 grams
Potassium Bromide	3 ounces	90.0 grams
Water to make	10 gallons	40.0 liters

Dissolve the sulfite in about one gallon (4 liters) of warm water (not over 125° F.) (52° C.). Pour about 3 quarts of this solution in the tank and add one gallon of warm water to the remaining quart of sulfite solution. Then dissolve the hydroquinone in this dilute sulfite solution and, when completely dissolved, add this solution to the tank. Now, dissolve the carbonate and the bromide in one gallon of warm water (not over 125° F.) (52° C.) and add to the tank. Add cold water immediately to make up to 10 gallons (40 liters). Stir the entire volume of solution with a paddle or a mechanical stirrer until thorough mixing is assured.

Mixing Concentrated Developers

The extent to which a developer may be concentrated is determined by the solubility of the least soluble constituent, because a stock solution should usually withstand cooling to 40° F. (4.4° C.) without any of the ingredients crystallizing out. (See Table of Solubilities, page 156.) Usually, the hydroquinone and Elon come out of solution on cooling, but this may be prevented by adding wood alcohol or methanol in a concentration up to 10%. Denatured alcohol may be used if wood alcohol has been added as the denaturant. If a precipitate forms, however, on adding the denatured alcohol to the developer, the denatured alcohol is unfit for use.

The addition of the alcohol does not prevent the other ingredients such as sodium sulfite from crystallizing out, in fact, the alcohol diminishes their solubility and therefore increases the tendency to come out of solution.

A para-aminophenol-carbonate developer is difficult to prepare in concentrated form, though by adding a little caustic soda the solubility of the para-aminophenol is increased and a stronger solution can thus be prepared.

When preparing concentrated developers it is important to observe carefully the rules of mixing, taking care to keep the temperature of the solution as low as possible if a colorless developer is to be obtained.

The following formula is a typical example of a concentrated developer and is prepared by dissolving the ingredients in the order given:

	Avoirdupois	Metric
Water (about 125° F.) (52° C.)	16 ounces	500.0 cc.
Elon	75 grains	5.1 grams
Sodium Sulfite, desiccated	2½ ounces	75.0 grams
Hydroquinone	¾ ounce	22.5 grams
Sodium Carbonate, desiccated	3½ ounces	105.0 grams
Potassium Bromide	38 grains	2.6 grams
Wood Alcohol	4¼ ounces	134.0 cc.
Cold water to make	32 ounces	1.0 liter

Two-Solution Developers

A two-solution developer is simply a one-solution developer split into two parts, one containing the alkali and bromide, the other containing the developing agent and preservative so that the developer will oxidize less readily and therefore keep well. The reason why it is customary to keep a developer like pyro in two solutions, is because pyro oxidizes much more readily than Elon or para-aminophenol with a given amount of preservative. (See also page 73.)

For purposes of mixing only one-solution developers need be considered because the same rules regarding mixing apply in both cases.

How to Prepare Fixing Solutions

Fixing baths may be divided into the following classes:

1. *Plain hypo solutions.*

2. *Acid fixing solutions* consisting of hypo with the addition of sodium bisulfite, potassium metabisulfite, or sodium sulfite with acid.

3. *Acid hardening fixing solutions.*

1. No difficulty is usually experienced when mixing a *plain hypo solution.* When mixing a quantity of solution in a tank, the filter bag method (page 65) should be used and the hypo dissolved in warm water because the temperature

drops considerably while the hypo is dissolving. If a scum forms on the surface of the solution on standing this should be removed by drawing the edge of a clean towel or blotter across the surface.

If a wooden cover is used for the tank, it should be waterproofed (as described below) to prevent the growth of fungi which produce acid substances that decompose the hypo, turning it milky. For best results the cover should be laminated in two layers so that the wood in each layer is fitted together at right angles. The two layers should then be fastened together with countersunk monel or 18-8 stainless steel screws.

Waterproofing may be accomplished by dipping the cover several times in a suitable lacquer solution. The cover should be allowed to dry between each dipping; and it should be examined subsequently at intervals and redipped when necessary.

The slime which occasionally forms on the inner surface of wooden tanks can be removed by washing the tank out at intervals with sodium hypochlorite solution as described in the section on "Cleaning Containers for Photographic Solutions," page 88.

A plain fixing bath, however, is seldom used because it gradually becomes alkaline from an accumulation of alkali carried over by prints and films from the developer and this tends to soften the gelatin, while the image continues to develop in the fixing bath, so that if two prints stick together, more development takes place at the point of contact, causing uneven development. If the bath is acid, the acid kills or neutralizes the alkali in the developer carried over, thus preventing unevenness.

2. *All acid fixing baths* contain either sodium bisulfite, potassium metabisulfite, or a mixture of sodium sulfite and a weak acid. The directions for mixing are as follows:

a. Do not add the bisulfite or acid sulfite solutions to the warm hypo solution or the hypo will turn milky. The solutions should be quite cold when mixed.

b. On keeping, an acid hypo solution gradually becomes milky, so that a stock solution of the sodium bisulfite, etc., should be kept and added to the plain hypo stock solution as required. For general purposes 1½ ozs. (45 cc.) of a 50% sodium bisulfite solution is added to 32 ozs. (one liter) of a 35% hypo solution. If any considerable excess over this amount is added, the hypo rapidly turns milky especially in warm weather, owing to the liberation of sulfur.

Formula F-24 on page 119 represents a satisfactory bisulfite fixing bath.

3. *Acid hardening fixing baths* are prepared by adding to hypo an acid hardening solution which contains the following ingredients:

a. An acid such as acetic, boric, citric, lactic, maleic, malic, sulfuric, tartaric, etc., which stops development.

b. A hardening agent such as potassium alum or potassium chrome alum.

c. A preservative such as sodium sulfite or sodium bisulfite. The latter acts as a preservative in two ways: It prevents the formation of sulfur by the action of the acid on the hypo, while it also prevents the developer carried over into the fixing bath from oxidizing and turning brown.

Prepare the acid hardening solution as a separate stock solution and add this to the hypo solution as required.

The order of mixing is important, as follows:

When mixing in one vessel, first dissolve the sulfite in warm water (about 125° F.) (52° C.), then add the acid and then the potassium alum. It is sometimes recommended to reverse the process, namely, dissolve the alum first, add the acid, and then the sulfite, but the alum dissolves more readily in the acid-sulfite solution.

Another method is to dissolve the alum and sulfite in separate solutions, cool, add the acid to the sulfite solution and then add the alum solution.

The hypo should be cool and dissolved completely before adding the cool hardener; otherwise sulfur is likely to be precipitated.

If the order of mixing is reversed and the alum added first to the sulfite a white sludge of aluminum sulfite is formed which dissolves with difficulty when the acid is added. Therefore, if after mixing, the hardener is milky and a sludge settles out it is due to a relative insufficiency of acid, that is, the acid used was either not up to strength or too much sulfite was added. Potassium alum fixing baths containing boric acid have the least propensity to sludge of any baths of this type. (Formulas F-5, F-10, and F-25, pages 115, 117, and 118.)

With other hardening baths the order of mixing is usually the same.

Fixing baths containing chrome alum as the hardening agent usually have sulfuric acid as the active acid. (See Formulas F-16 and F-23, pages 117 and 118.) No difficulty should be found in mixing the bath providing care is taken in adding the sulfuric acid to the chrome alum solution. The acid should be poured slowly down the side of the mixing vessel while stirring the chrome alum solution to insure thorough mixing, since this acid is very heavy and will sink to the bottom if not mixed well. *Water should never be added to the sulfuric acid or the solution may boil and spatter some of the acid on the hands or face causing serious burns.*

Storage of Chemicals

Chemicals should be stored in well corked or well stoppered bottles or tightly covered jars in a cool, dry place because most chemicals are affected by air, which contains oxygen, carbon dioxide gas and moisture.

(a) Oxygen readily attacks such substances as sodium sulfite, especially in the presence of moisture, converting it into sodium sulfate, which is useless as a preservative. With crystallized sodium sulfite the sodium sulfate forms on the outside of the crystals as a powder, which may be washed off and the crystals dried. It is not easy to detect sodium sulfate in desiccated sulfite except by chemical tests.

Other substances which combine with oxygen and are, therefore, said to be oxidized, are sodium bisulfite and potassium metabisulfite and all developing agents such as pyro, hydroquinone, etc., which turn more or less brown, the extent of the color roughly indicating the degree of oxidation.

(b) Carbon dioxide gas combines with substances like caustic soda and caustic potash, converting them into the corresponding carbonated alkalis which are less reactive. If sodium hydroxide is kept in a glass stoppered bottle the stopper usually becomes cemented fast by the sodium carbonate formed, so that it should be kept in a rubber stoppered bottle. Owing to the solvent action of the caustic alkalis on glass the inside of the glass bottle containing caustic or strongly carbonated solutions becomes frosted, though the quantity of glass thus dissolved away will usually do no harm.

(c) Certain chemicals have a strong attraction or affinity for the moisture in the atmosphere and gradually dissolve in the water thus absorbed, forming a solution. This phenomenon is termed "deliquescence" and the chemicals are said to be "deliquescent." Familiar examples are ammonium thiocyanate, potassium carbonate, sodium sulfide, uranyl nitrate, sodium bichromate, etc., which should be stored in corked bottles and the neck dipped in melted paraffin wax.

As mentioned earlier (page 52), it is difficult to prepare a solution of definite percentage strength from a chemical which has deliquesced, though it is usually sufficient to drain off the crystals, or to use a hydrometer at a definite temperature, referring to a table giving the hydrometer readings in terms of percentage strength.

(d) While some chemicals absorb moisture as above, others give up their water of crystallization to the atmosphere, and therefore lose their crystalline shape and fall to a powder and are then said to "effloresce," the phenomenon being termed "efflorescence." Some crystals do not contain any water and therefore cannot effloresce.

A very dry atmosphere is suitable, therefore, for storing deliquescent salts but not for efflorescent salts. The only way to store such chemicals is to isolate them from the air suitably by sealing.

(e) Some chemicals are decomposed by long exposure to light, especially sunlight. Such chemicals usually change more rapidly when made up as a solution than when stored in the solid form. Silver nitrate is probably the outstanding example. Crystals of this salt darken in light and a solution will darken quite rapidly. The remedy is to store both the solid and liquid in dark brown bottles. Potassium iodide solutions often turn a deep yellow color because of the liberation of free iodine. Nitric acid sometimes turns yellowish brown on standing in white bottles for long periods of time. Potassium ferricyanide solution turns blue on prolonged exposure to light owing to the formation of Prussian blue.

Stock solutions and developers should be stored in either hard glazed earthenware crocks, large glass bottles, wooden vats, or tanks of resistant material, and so arranged that the liquid may be drawn off at the side and near the bottom. (See section on "Apparatus," page 55.)

In case a solution such as Pyro has to be stored for a long time and withdrawn at intervals, an absorption bottle containing alkaline pyro may be fitted at the intake which absorbs oxygen from the air as it enters the bottle on withdrawing part of the solution.

PREPARING SOLUTIONS

Hard glazed earthenware crocks are most satisfactory for storage of stock solutions of developers and fixing baths for volumes of 5 gallons (20 liters) or more. The crocks should be fitted with lacquered wooden covers. (See page 67.) The method of attaching the outlet is important. If not supplied with a hole slightly above the base, the crock should be drilled. A hard rubber tube should then be inserted through a soft rubber stopper and the tube and stopper fastened securely to the jar by passing a monel or 18-8 stainless steel band around it. A short length of pure gum rubber tubing may be fastened over the end of the outlet tube and closed by means of a screw clamp or a hard rubber faucet may be fitted on the hard rubber tube. Large glass bottles, although more susceptible to breakage, may also be used as containers, and these should be fitted in a similar way with hard rubber tube outlets.

A battery of stock solution bottles or crocks may be arranged on lead covered shelves under which an 18-8 Mo stainless steel trough is placed, or, the floor may be arranged to form a sink so that in case of accidental breakage no serious damage is done. This precaution is of special importance in the case of hypo solutions, which might percolate into various rooms in a studio or laboratory and inoculate them with hypo dust, causing an epidemic of spots.

Wooden storage tanks may be reinforced against leaking by coating their inner surfaces with asphalt (M.P. 250° to 300° F.), or Kodacoat paint as described under the section on "Apparatus," pages 55 and 56.

CHAPTER IX

USING SOLUTIONS

Photographic solutions, especially developers, vary considerably in their period of usefulness or time during which they may be utilized effectively to process exposed films and papers. This "useful life" as it is sometimes called, is, therefore, an important property of a solution and should be studied by everyone handling photographic materials. There are a good many factors which influence the useful life of a solution, such as whether it receives intermittent or continuous use, the extent of the surface exposed to the air, the temperature, the nature and reactions of the chemical constituents, and the manipulative procedure used in handling films or prints in the bath.

The average photographic solution is usually discarded as soon as its working rate is reduced to an impractical time period. Methods of reviving developers are somewhat vague and much work remains to be done on this subject. In the case of certain tank developers it is customary to add a replenisher solution several times before the developer is discarded. More is known about the revival of fixing baths however, but with these solutions it is usually safer and more economical, except in specific cases, to discard them after a certain period of usefulness than to bother with revival.

A new type of potassium alum fixing bath containing boric acid does not require revival except when used with strongly alkaline developers, because the bath does not sludge readily and has better hardening properties than earlier formulas. (See Formulas F-5 and F-25, pages 115 and 118.)

Some workers use solutions for several years merely by withdrawing a part of the used bath and adding fresh solution at regular intervals. Though this practice has some merit it is generally to be condemned since most photographic solutions accumulate certain reaction products that greatly reduce their efficiency and in addition may have harmful effects.

This chapter contains a summary of the characteristics of developers and fixing baths both with and without use, a discussion of troubles, the effect of temperature on solutions, and methods of cleaning containers for photographic solutions.

The Useful Life of Developers

Without Use. If a freshly mixed developer (prepared with water boiled to free it from dissolved air) is stored in a completely filled and stoppered or wax-corked bottle, it will keep almost indefinitely even in the light. Under ordinary conditions of storage, the bottle or vessel contains more or less air. Also, when an ordinary cork or a non-airtight cover is used, the surface of the developer is continually in contact with air, the oxygen constituent of which oxidizes the developing agent and sodium sulfite present. This results in a lowering of the developing power in direct proportion to the amount of oxidation of the developing agent, which is accelerated as the preservative or sodium sulfite becomes oxidized also.

The oxidation products of developing agents are usually colored so that the developer on keeping frequently turns brown. In the presence of sodium sulfite, however, the oxidation products of hydroquinone may consist of hydroquinone mono- and di-sodium sulfonates which are colorless. The fact that an old Elon-hydroquinone developer is colorless is, therefore, no indication that the original developing power is unimpaired. An oxidized Elon or Elon-hydroquinone developer also frequently fluoresces strongly.

In some cases when an Elon-hydroquinone developer gives slight developer fog when freshly mixed, the fogging tendency disappears on standing. This may be due to the anti-aerial fogging action of the developer oxidation products which are produced on keeping. (See paragraph on fog under "Developer Troubles," page 75.)

A solution of a developing agent, such as pyro, to be stored for a considerable time, will keep best in the presence of an acid sulfite such as sodium bisulfite rather than sodium sulfite which is slightly alkaline. It is always preferable therefore to prepare such a developer as two solutions: one containing the developing agent and sodium bisulfite, and the other the carbonate and bromide, and to mix these solutions as required for use. A plain solution of sodium sulfite oxidizes readily in contact with air at a concentration below 10%, but above this concentration it oxidizes very slowly. Stock solutions containing sodium sulfite alone or in combination with a developing agent should be prepared, so that the concentration of the sulfite is around 10% for maximum keeping properties. Owing to the relative insolubility of Elon in a sodium sulfite solution, it is not possible to prepare such stock solutions with Elon.

Sodium bisulfite keeps satisfactorily in more dilute solutions and is a better preservative than sulfite in the absence of carbonate. It is usual therefore to keep readily oxidizable developing agents such as pyro, amidol, etc., by mixing with sodium bisulfite. On adding sodium carbonate to sodium bisulfite, sodium sulfite and sodium bicarbonate are formed, so that in compounding a two-solution formula from a one-solution formula it is necessary to take care of this neutralization of the carbonate by using an extra quantity.

Single solution developers containing sodium hydroxide or potassium hydroxide do not keep unless well stoppered; pure gum rubber stoppers being most suitable.

With Use. During development, several reactions are taking place: (1) The developing agent and sulfite are being oxidized by the air; (2) the developing agent is being destroyed as a result of performing useful work in reducing the exposed silver halide emulsion to metallic silver; and (3) oxidation products of the developer and the by-products, sodium bromide and sodium iodide, are accumulating. The bromide and iodide and developer oxidation products restrain development while the oxidation products prevent aerial fog. The restraining action of the bromide and iodide is analogous to cutting down the exposure, so that with an old developer it is not possible even on prolonged development to get the ultimate result out of an under-exposure.

Testing a Tank Developer. One of the most satisfactory methods of testing a tank developer consists in printing from a standard master positive using a controlled exposure and comparing the quality of the developed negative obtained with that of a standard negative of good quality. The developed negative should match the standard both with regard to (a) highlight density, and (b) shadow detail. If the highlight density, which largely determines the contrast, (if fog is low), is weak, this indicates the need of either more time for development or more replenisher, or both. If the contrast is equal to that of the standard but there is a considerable loss of shadow detail, this indicates that the developer has accumulated an excess of restraining products, and a fresh developer should be prepared.*

The time required to produce a definite contrast increases as a developer is used, and the solution ceases to be useful when the time required for this exceeds the maximum time which can be allotted for the developing operation. A deep tank developer, for example, is therefore discarded for one or more of the following reasons: (1) The time for complete development is excessively long; (2) The solution stains or fogs emulsions badly; and (3) The accumulation of by-products is so great that shadow detail is lost even with full development.

Developer Troubles

The Developer Gives Fog. Fog is the chief trouble caused by faulty mixing. It may be a result of violation of the rules of mixing such as dissolving the carbonate before the sulfite, mixing the solution too hot, omitting the bromide, adding too much carbonate or too little sulfite, the use of impure chemicals, etc.

With certain developers, notably those containing Elon and hydroquinone, a form of fog, known as *aerial* fog, is produced when film wet with developing solution is exposed to the air. Motion picture positive film developed on a reel is especially sensitive to aerial fog. It may be prevented by adding about 5% of old developer to the freshly mixed developer. This is more effective than increasing the concentration of bromide above the normal quantity added. The oxidized developer probably acts as an anti-fogging agent thus reducing the tendency for fog formation.

Negatives developed in a developer containing an excess of sulfite or one containing hypo or ammonia may show *dichroic* or *green fog*. This appears yellowish-green by reflected light, and a pink color by transmitted light. It is usually caused when the dissolved silver salts, under certain conditions, are reduced to metallic silver in a very fine state of subdivision, particularly in the shadow portions of the negative where no bromide is liberated during development. Fine grained emulsions are most susceptible to this form of fog. Information on prevention and removal of dichroic

*The Eastman Kodak Company supplies a Testing Outfit consisting of a standard master positive and a standard negative. This outfit will enable any worker using tank development to test the developer solution quickly and accurately.

fog is given in an article "Stains on Negatives and Prints," obtainable from the Sales Service Division, Eastman Kodak Co., Rochester, N. Y.

Some deep tank developers may begin to fog a short time after they have been put into use. When this occurs it usually can be traced to the presence of sulfide in the solution caused by the action of bacteria which reduced the sulfite in the developer to sulfide. The fog may be cleared up by putting some waste film or plates through the solution or by adding a small quantity of lead acetate to the developer (60 grains per gallon or one gram per liter). The bacteria or fungi usually grow in the slimy deposit which accumulates on the inner walls of the tank. This deposit may be removed by sterilizing the container occasionally with bleaching powder. (See section on Cleaning Containers for Photographic Solutions, page 88).

The Solution is Colored. As a general rule, the developer when mixed should be colorless, or nearly so and if colored very much it should be suspected as being likely to give fog. In the case of a pyro developer mixed with bisulfite, which contains iron, an inky substance is formed as a combination product of the iron and the pyro, and this imparts a dirty bluish-red color to the solution although photographically it is harmless. If a two-solution pyro developer is mixed in dirty vessels the B solution (which contains the carbonate and bromide) may be colored brown by the presence of a little pyro.

The Solution Does Not Develop. Omission of the developing agent or the carbonate may usually be suspected if a developer does not develop.

Precipitation of a White Sludge. If a white precipitate settles on standing, this is probably Elon. The precipitate may often be redissolved by adding 5% of wood alcohol or methanol, but if this is not successful, then the formula contains either too much Elon or sulfite or not enough carbonate. If it is known that the formula gives a clear solution when mixed correctly and should the Elon precipitate out during mixing when the sulfite is added, the precipitate will usually redissolve on adding the carbonate. If the final solution is not colored, no harm will have been done.

Scum. Scum may be picked up on films or plates from the surface of the developer especially if the solution has been allowed to stand unused for several days. The scum may consist of grease, solid matter, or developer oxidation products, especially if the developer contains pyro. The scum should be removed by passing the edge of a sheet of blotting paper along the surface of the solution or by using a skimmer, consisting of several layers of cheese cloth stretched over a wire frame.

Miscellaneous Troubles. Various types of developer stains may be produced on films, plates, and papers. These are discussed in detail in the article on "Stains" referred to on page 76. When a developer solution is not agitated sufficiently during the progress of development, characteristic markings are produced. This is occasionally observed with film developed on hangers or racks. These markings are usually the result of retardation of development along the sides of a hanger or rack caused by the accumulation of oxidized developer products and sodium bromide. They may be prevented by thorough agitation of the holder or rack during development.

The Importance of Rinsing

It is important to rinse films, plates and papers after development and before fixation. When a film or print is transferred from the developer directly to the fixing bath the alkali in the developer retained by the film or print neutralizes some of the acid of the fixing bath. The addition of developer also gradually destroys the hardening properties of the fixing bath. Therefore, by removing as much developer as possible from the film or print by thoroughly rinsing in water or an acid rinse bath for 10 or 20 seconds, the life of the fixing bath is very much prolonged, while the tendency for stains and blisters to form is very much reduced.

Rinsing and Hardening Films or Plates. In warm weather it is only possible to rinse films or plates in water for one or 2 seconds; otherwise the gelatin will soften. If the chrome alum hardening bath (Formula SB-3, page 70) is used, rinsing in water may be omitted although a previous rinse for a few seconds in water will prolong the life of this bath also. The negative material should be left in the bath 3 minutes to insure adequate hardening. *Films or plates should be agitated for several seconds after putting in the hardening bath; otherwise a chromium scum, which is difficult to remove is apt to form on the film.* This scum is composed of chromium hydroxide and is produced by the reaction between the chrome alum and the alkaline developer carried over on the film, but it does not form with a fresh bath if the film is well agitated on immersion. When the bath becomes old, a scum will tend to form even if the films are agitated; the bath should then be discarded. *Films should always be wiped with wetted cotton* after washing to remove any possible traces of scum, because once the film is dry it is impossible to remove it.

The hardening bath is a blue color by artificial light when freshly mixed, but it ultimately turns yellowish-green with use. *It then ceases to harden and should be replaced by a fresh bath.*

Rinsing Prints. Thorough rinsing will largely prevent staining troubles with prints and will allow a larger number to be fixed before the bath sludges. An acid rinse or "short stop" bath is strongly recommended instead of a water rinse because it arrests development immediately, whereas, when rinsing in water, development of the print continues if the rinsing is unduly prolonged.

When handling only a few prints, a rinse of 5 to 10 seconds is sufficient, but if large batches of prints are being processed, the rinsing time should be from one to 2 minutes. It is important to move the prints and see that they are separated while in the acetic acid rinse bath (Formula SB-1 page 114), and in the fixing bath to insure that the solutions have thorough access to all parts of every print. If prints are not rinsed, developer is carried over to the fixing bath and the alkali in the developer rapidly neutralizes the acid in the fixing bath. When a certain quantity of developer has been carried over, a white sludge forms and the bath becomes alkaline. Prints fixed in an alkaline bath are likely to become stained brown. When an acid rinse bath is used, no harm is done if the prints are left in the rinse bath 10 or 20 minutes.

When an acid rinse bath is used, sludging of the fixing bath will never occur if the rinse bath is always kept acid. A simple method of testing whether the bath is alkaline or acid is to dip a strip of blue litmus paper in the bath. If the paper turns red, the bath is acid, but if it remains blue, the bath is alkaline and should then be discarded.

The life of the acid rinse bath (Formula SB-1, page 114) used for papers is determined by the quantity of alkali carried over from the developer, which depends on the quantity of carbonate in the developer, the quantity of developer retained by the print, and the time of draining. With a 1- to

2-seconds drain and a typical Elon-hydroquinone developer, the equivalent of approximately eighty 8 x 10-in. prints per gallon (ninety 3¼ x 5½-in. prints per quart) may be processed safely in the acid rinse bath before the bath becomes alkaline.

The Properties of Fixing Baths

A plain solution of hypo is seldom used as a fixing bath but it is usually used in conjunction with a weakly acid salt such as sodium bisulfite, or more commonly with an acid hardening solution. The standard hardener contains a preservative, sodium sulfite, which prevents decomposition of the hypo; an acid, usually acetic acid, to neutralize any alkali carried over in the film from the developer and thereby arrest development; and a hardening agent, either potassium alum or chromium alum. Some potassium alum fixing baths contain boric acid in addition to acetic acid. The addition of boric acid extends the hardening life of the bath and minimizes greatly the sludging tendency. (See Formulas F-5 and F-25, pages 115 and 118.)

A satisfactory acid hardening fixing bath should have certain properties, namely, a fairly rapid rate of fixation, good hardening, a long sludging life, and a long "useful" life. The time for fixation is usually taken as twice the time for the milkiness or opalescence of the unreduced silver salts to disappear. This depends on the strength of the hypo (30% to 40% fixes most rapidly), the photographic material tested (portrait films fix in about 3 to 5 minutes whereas lantern slides clear in 30 seconds to one minute), the temperature of the solution (65° F. or 18° C. is recommended), and the degree of exhaustion of the solution.

The hardening properties are influenced by a large number of factors. A certain minimum quantity of alum is required to give the necessary hardening, while an excess of alum may produce too much hardening and induce brittleness. Normal fixing baths such as Formula F-5, page 115, are compounded carefully to give a hardening of 180° to 200°F. (82° to 93° C.). This is determined by immersing a strip of the fixed and washed film in water and heating the water slowly until the gelatin flows away from the support. For maximum hardening using a 5-seconds rinse in water between development and fixation, and washing one hour in running water after fixation, films should be fixed 15 to 20 minutes in either fresh or partially exhausted fixing baths.

Properly compounded chrome alum fixing baths compare favorably in their hardening properties and useful life with fixing baths containing potassium alum. Chrome alum fixing baths lose their hardening properties, however, as developer is carried into the bath because of the resulting increase in sulfite concentration. If a thorough water rinse is used between development and fixation, no trouble from this cause should occur with properly compounded baths.

A good fixing bath should not sludge during its useful life when used at 65° to 70° F. (18° to 21° C.). Changes in temperature of the fixing bath affect the rate of fixation and the useful life of the solution. For example, if a film requires 95 seconds to clear at 65° F. (18° C.), it would take about 60 seconds to clear at 85° F. (29° C.), but it is dangerous practice to allow the temperature of the bath to rise above 70° F. (21° C.) as the solution is apt to precipitate sulfur.

A different technic must be used for processing at high temperatures, where the secret lies in preventing abnormal swelling of the gelatin, for once it is swollen it is almost impossible to reduce it and to handle the film. For more complete information on this subject, the booklet "Tropical Development" should be consulted. This is obtainable on request from the Sales Service Division, Eastman Kodak Company, Rochester, N. Y.

The Useful Life of Fixing Baths

A fixing bath in use becomes exhausted as a result of performing useful work in fixing out the emulsion. The acidity of the bath is being reduced by the developer carried in, although at first this tends to favor a longer "sulfurization life" or period of time before the bath precipitates sulfur. With use, however, the older type of bath finally reaches a point where a sludge of aluminum sulfite is precipitated, rendering the bath useless. During the first stages of use, the hardening properties increase slightly, after which they fall off rapidly. With the improved fixing bath containing boric acid, the bath does not sludge during its useful life with normally alkaline developers, and the hardening properties are maintained satisfactorily. The bath does not need to be discarded until the rate of fixation is too slow or the solution shows a tendency to stain the gelatin. When the time of clearing for a slow fixing film exceeds 12 to 15 minutes, the bath should be discarded.

Formulas F-5, F-10 and F-25 on pages 115, 117 and 118 will fix completely the equivalent of eighty to one hundred

USING SOLUTIONS

8 x 10-inch films or plates per gallon (4 liters) of solution, before the time to clear becomes excessive. The chrome alum baths, Formulas F-16 and F-23, on page 117 and 118, do not have quite as long a useful life because they tend to lose their hardening properties before the clearing time becomes excessive. The chrome alum fixing baths therefore require more frequent renewal than baths containing potassium alum and boric acid.

Formula F-1, on page 119, will fix sixty 8 x 10-inch prints per gallon, provided a thorough water rinse (at least 15 seconds) precedes fixation. If the prints are placed for at least 5 seconds in the acid rinse bath (Formula SB-1, page 114) between development and fixation, the F-1 fixing bath will not sludge so rapidly and the equivalent of one hundred and twenty 8 x 10-inch prints may be fixed safely per gallon.

These figures have been established by careful tests with moderately alkaline developers and it is recommended that the fixing bath be discarded and replaced by a fresh bath when approximately this number of films or prints have been fixed.

When strongly alkaline developers are used, the life of the fixing bath will be shortened correspondingly. Baths containing boric acid (Formulas F-5 and F-25) will last longer under these conditions than other types of baths.

For greatest permanence of prints after fixing, place them for 5 minutes in a fresh fixing bath and then wash for at least two hours in a tray where the wash water is flowing at such a rate as to replace the water in the tray at least 10 to 12 times per hour.

Recovery of Silver from Exhausted Fixing Baths

An exhausted fixing bath contains dissolved silver salts and various methods may be employed to recover the silver profitably, providing at least 5 gallons of well exhausted hypo are discarded each week. For large volumes of exhausted baths (about 100 gallons or more per week) precipitation with sodium sulfide is the most economical and rapid method. Precipitation with zinc dust is efficient when smaller volumes of bath are to be treated, and has the advantage that no objectionable fumes of hydrogen sulfide are evolved, as in the sulfide process.

Recovery by means of commercial electrolytic units also represents a simple and economical procedure for volumes of exhausted baths of not less than 100 gallons per week.

Electrolytic units give best results when used in a discarded fixing bath, rather than in a working bath.

Large scale electrolytic methods of silver recovery have been worked out by the Kodak Research Laboratories and units installed in several motion picture and photofinishing plants. Economical operation requires treatment of at least 400 gallons of fixing bath weekly in motion picture laboratories, and 100 gallons weekly in photofinishing plants. Details concerning these installations may be obtained upon application to the Eastman Kodak Company, Rochester, New York.

Although it is possible for a capable chemist, so to restore a fixing bath by desilvering, subsequently clarifying, and modifying its composition, that its useful life is prolonged, it is just as economical and preferable to prepare a fresh bath.

Fixing Bath Troubles

A. *Sludging of the Fixing Bath:* A fixing bath occasionally turns milky soon after the hardener is added, and sometimes after being in use for a short time. The milkiness may be of two kinds:

1. If the precipitate is *pale yellow* and settles very slowly on standing, it consists of sulfur and may be caused by (a) too much acid in the hardener; (b) too little sulfite or the use of impure sulfite, in which case there is not sufficient present to protect the hypo from the acid; (c) high temperature. The hardener should only be added to the hypo solution when at room temperature. If the temperature of the acid fixing bath is over 85° F. (29° C.), it will not remain clear longer than a few days even when mixed correctly. The only remedy is to throw the bath away and mix fresh solution as required.

If a sulfurized bath is used, the sulfur is apt to penetrate the gelatin, and later may cause fading of the image.

2. If the precipitate is *white*, and a gelatinous sludge of aluminum sulfite settles on standing, it may be caused by (a) too little acid in the hardener; for example, supposing a formula calls for pure glacial acetic acid and 28% acid is used by mistake, then less than one-third the required concentration of acid is present; (b) too little hardener in the fixing bath. When fixing prints, a relatively large proportion of the developer is carried over to the fixing bath (unless a water or acid rinse bath has been used) which soon neutralizes the acid, and therefore increases the tendency for precipita-

tion of aluminum sulfite. In the same way a fixing bath with the correct proportion of hardener, when exhausted, still contains alum and sulfite but no acid, and these combine to form a sludge of aluminum sulfite.

It is extremely important, to use only the acid specified and to know its strength, *because trouble is caused if more or less acid is used than is called for in the formula.* It has been found that the hardening properties of an alum-acid fixing bath bear a relation to the tendency of the bath to precipitate aluminum sulfite. In other words, a bath containing an excess of acid (and which therefore may be used for a relatively long time before the aluminum sulfite precipitates), does not harden as well as a bath which precipitates when a much smaller volume of developer is added. With such a bath containing a minimum of acid it is advisable to add a further quantity of acid as soon as a slight precipitate appears; a satisfactory quantity being about one-half that originally present in the bath.

With potassium alum fixing baths containing boric acid, the tendency for precipitation of aluminum sulfite is greatly minimized and sludging does not usually occur unless a large volume of developer is added directly to the fixing bath.

B. *The bath does not harden satisfactorily.* Insufficient hardening may be a result of (1) the use of inferior alum which does not contain the correct proportion of aluminum sulfate; (2) the presence of too much acid or sulfite; or (3) an insufficient quantity of alum. On varying the proportions of acid, alum and sulfite in a fixing bath, it has been found that the hardening increases as the quantity of alum increases. With increasing quantities of acetic acid, with a given quantity of alum, the hardening increases to a maximum, beyond which it decreases until the solution does not harden at all. Similarly with boric acid, in a bath containing acetic acid, increasing the concentration of boric acid produces both an increase in the hardening and an extension of the hardening life. A certain minimum quantity of acetic acid, however, is necessary to give the fixing bath a fairly long, useful life, before aluminum sulfite precipitates, but this quantity is usually greater than the quantity which produces maximum hardening. With use, therefore, the hardening ability of most fixing baths at first increases to a maximum, with the addition of developer, beyond which the hardening falls off rapidly.

C. *Blisters.* When the sodium carbonate in a developer

is neutralized by the acid in the fixing bath, carbon dioxide gas is evolved which produces blisters if the gelatin is too soft to withstand the disruptive action of the gas. If the fixing bath contains an excess of acid and the films are not rinsed sufficiently, or if a strongly acid rinse bath is used, blisters are apt to be formed. On dry film, blisters appear as tiny crater-like depressions when examined by reflected light. This trouble is more liable to occur in hot weather, and especially when the bath is not hardening sufficiently.

Trouble from blisters may be avoided by using *Kodalk* as the alkali in the developer, because this substance does not react with the acid in the fixing bath to liberate gas.

D. *Dichroic Fog.* If the fixing bath does not contain acid or if it is old and exhausted and contains an excess of dissolved silver salts, a stain called *dichroic fog* is sometimes produced on the film. In reflected light, film stained in this way appears yellowish-green and by transmitted light it looks reddish-pink. Dichroic fog never occurs in a fresh acid fixing bath, or if the film is rinsed before fixing and the temperature of the bath is kept at 65° to 70° F. (18° to 21° C.). Methods of removal of dichroic fog are discussed in the booklet, "Stains on Negatives and Prints" obtainable from the Sales Service Division, Eastman Kodak Company, Rochester, N. Y.

E. *Scum on Fixing Baths.* When a partially exhausted fixing bath is allowed to stand several days without use, the hydrogen sulfide gas usually present in the air reacts with the silver thiosulfate in the bath and forms a metallic appearing scum on the surface of the solution. This scum consists of silver sulfide and should be removed by drawing the edge of a sheet of blotting paper across the surface of the bath, or by using a skimmer made of several strips of cheesecloth stretched over a wire frame.

A white scum consisting of aluminum sulfite is found sometimes on films or prints. This is caused by: (1) insufficient rinsing after development; (2) too low a concentration of acid in the fixing bath; (3) insufficient agitation of the film on first immersing in the fixing bath. Since aluminum sulfite is soluble in alkali, the scum may be removed by swabbing the film or print with a 10% solution of sodium carbonate and then washing thoroughly.

Trouble from scum formation may be decreased by using fixing baths containing boric acid, because such baths have a minimum tendency to precipitate an aluminum sulfite sludge.

With chrome alum fixing baths, a scum composed of chromium hydroxide is produced as described under the section on "The Importance of Rinsing," page 77. Films which are fixed in such a bath should always be wiped carefully with wetted cotton for if any chromium scum dries on the surface it is impossible to remove it. A chrome alum fixing bath is not recommended for use with papers because of its slight staining characteristics.

F. *Stains.* Several different types of stains such as white aluminum sulfite stain (see E, page 84), sulfur stains, and yellow silver stains, are occasionally produced. For a complete discussion of fixing bath stains reference should be made to the article "Stains on Negatives and Prints," obtainable from the Sales Service Division, Eastman Kodak Company, Rochester, N. Y.

G. *Mottle.* When processing film or plates in hangers, a mottled image is occasionally found when the hanger has not been agitated enough on first immersing in the fixing bath, or if the film is insufficiently rinsed between development and fixation. In the absence of thorough rinsing and agitation, development continues locally during the first few minutes of fixing and in these spots the image has greater density. Mottle is also produced if the ends of the hanger protrude above the surface of the fixing bath, especially during the first stages of fixation.

Effect of Temperature on Chemicals and Solutions

Nearly all chemicals used in photographic work have a high enough melting point so that there is little danger of the solids melting while stored in bottles or other containers, but it is good practice to keep storage bottles dry and cool. Bottles or cans, for instance, should not be placed on shelves or in cupboards near a stove or where direct sunlight can shine upon them.

When in solution the effect of temperature on chemicals is much greater and must be taken into account with every photographic solution. Under normal working conditions, a temperature of 65° F. (18° C.) is recommended for negative development, and 70° F. (21° C.) for print development.

In photographic practice, temperatures of solutions are measured either by the Centigrade or Fahrenheit thermometer. On the Centigrade thermometer water freezes at zero and boils at 100 degrees, and on the Fahrenheit scale the corresponding readings are 32 degrees and 212 degrees, so that 100 degrees C. are equivalent to 212 degrees minus 32 degrees or 180 degrees F., that is, one degree C. is equivalent to 9/5 degrees F.

To convert degrees Centigrade to Fahrenheit, multiply by 9/5 and add 32. To convert degrees Fahrenheit to Centigrade subtract 32 and divide by 9/5.

On the continent of Europe, the Reaumer scale is used extensively although most scientific laboratories employ the Centigrade scale. Many thermometers are calibrated in both scales. The values on the Reaumer scale differ from the Centigrade values in the proportion 4:5.

Most chemical reactions proceed more rapidly as the temperature is increased, and this is true of all the reactions involved in photography, so that developers and fixing baths will act much more rapidly when warm than when cold. Different reactions are stimulated to different extents by rise of temperature, and the effect of temperature can be measured numerically, the result obtained being termed the "temperature coefficient" of the reaction.

As a general rule, the temperature coefficient is measured for a change of temperature of 10 degrees Centigrade, equivalent to 18 degrees Fahrenheit. Therefore, if a reaction takes 4 minutes at 60° F. (15° C.) and is completed in 2 minutes at 78° F. (25° C.) it is said to have a temperature coefficient of 2, the rate of reaction being doubled for a rise of 18° F. (10° C.).

The temperature coefficient of development varies with the developing agent, being least with the developers of high reduction potential, such as Elon, and most with developers of low reduction potential, such as hydroquinone. There is one consequence of this which is rather important, namely, that the behavior of a mixed hydroquinone developer depends upon the temperature. At low temperature the hydroquinone is very inert, while the Elon is not decreased in its rate of action to the same extent, and consequently the developer behaves as if it contained an excess of Elon. At high temperatures the hydroquinone is increased in its activity far more than the Elon, and the situation is reversed.

A similar principle applies to the fogging produced by developers. If development is continued for a sufficient time all developers will fog, but the fog reaction is a different one to that of development, and apparently has a different temperature coefficient and one which is much higher than the temperature coefficient of the development reaction itself. Consequently, a developer which will develop a material to a good density with low fog at a normal temperature, may produce very bad fog if the temperature is high.

From the above it will be understood that the control of temperature in photography is of great importance and that so far as possible development and fixation should always be carried out at a normal temperature (65° to 70° F.) (18° to 21° C.), a serious change in temperature involving much greater care and the risk of difficulty. If the temperature is too high, then trouble may be encountered with fog and with softening and frilling of the material, while if the temperature is too low, development will be delayed, there is danger of under-development, and fixing will be slow so that the greatest care must be taken to insure thorough fixation.

Fixing baths frequently decompose very rapidly with liberation of free sulfur if kept for a few hours to a few days at temperatures over 95°F. (35° C.). Although the rate of fixation is increased at higher temperatures, it is very bad practice to allow the temperature of a fixing bath to rise above 75° F. (24° C.); the recommended temperature being 65° F. (18 °C.). In storing large volumes of fixing bath it is best to store the hypo and hardener solutions separately and add the cool hardener to the cool hypo when the latter is put into a working tank.

Some strongly oxidizing solutions, acid permanganate, in particular, when employed at high temperatures rapidly lose their effectiveness for photographic use owing to secondary reactions. Usually these solutions work best at temperatures below 70° F. (21° C.).

Some photographic solutions, notably a hypo alum toning bath, are recommended to be used at 120° F. (49° C.), but even these solutions should be watched carefully to see that the temperature does not rise above that recommended, otherwise blistering, staining, and degradation of tone will result.

About the best general rule for temperature is to mix, store, and use the solutions at the temperature recommended in the manufacturer's instructions.

When the temperature cannot be controlled, as may be the case in the tropics, special measures must be taken as described completely in the booklet, "Tropical Development" obtainable on request from the Sales Service Division, Eastman Kodak Company, Rochester, N. Y.

Cleaning Containers for Photographic Solutions

Apparatus used for mixing and containing photographic chemicals becomes discolored and sometimes coated with decomposition products of the solution. In certain cases this does no harm, especially if the container is always used for the same kind of solution, but it is much better technic to clean all containers each time they are emptied. With cheaper containers, such as bottles and old trays, it is not worth wasting time if these are difficult to clean. It is better to discard the container and use a new one.

Most cleaning solutions are either strong alkalis or acids, and should be used with the same discretion given these chemicals when mixing photographic solutions. The principle of a cleaning solution is that it acts on the stain or deposit and changes it to a soluble form, which dissolves in the cleaning agent, or may be washed out with water. Sometimes the cleaning agent merely softens the deposit sufficiently so that it may be removed by the use of a wire brush or an abrading substance like sand or glass beads.

The most common tray cleaner is an acid solution of potassium bichromate made by dissolving potassium bichromate in water, and adding concentrated sulfuric acid. (See Formula TC-1, page 143.) This solution will remove stains, caused by oxidation products of developers, silver stains, and some dye stains, and is a very useful cleaning agent. Care should be used when handling any strong alkali or acid.

Other solutions which will be found useful are 1% permanganate, (followed by treatment in 50% bisulfite to remove the residual brown manganese stain); 40% sodium hydroxide (caustic soda); and any of the strong mineral acids, such as sulfuric, hydrochloric, and nitric. After removal of the stain, the vessel should be washed thoroughly to insure complete removal of the cleaning agent.

When an acid fixing bath sulfurizes, the colloidal sulfur is quite difficult to remove with a cleaning agent, but the addition of glass beads or sand to the bottle or other vessel with shaking will be found effective. A hot, concentrated solution of sodium sulfite (about 20%) will also usually dissolve sulfur.

Enamelled trays or tanks which have been used with strongly alkaline developers or caustic solutions, rapidly lose their glossy surface and become roughened and discolor easi-

USING SOLUTIONS

ly. If such containers are used with dye solutions, the dye is taken up in the pores of the enamel, and it is a very difficult matter to remove it completely. Trays badly discolored in this way are not worth the time to clean them.

Large tanks of wood, Alberene, or stoneware, after several weeks of use as developer containers, become coated with a layer of slime or mold which should be cleaned out by thoroughly scrubbing the walls with a wire brush, and then treating either with chloride of lime or sodium hypochlorite solution. The hypochlorite solution should be added to the tank in the following proportion: one part of stock hypochlorite solution to 6 parts of water. After the solution has been left in the tank overnight it should be emptied out and the tank given another thorough scrubbing and several washings previous to being put into service again. A stock solution of hypochlorite is prepared by making up a 4% solution of calcium hypochlorite and converting this into sodium hypochlorite. To prepare this solution, sodium carbonate solution (10%) is added to the calcium hypochlorite solution until no more precipitate forms, and the solution is then allowed to stand until all the precipitate settles to the bottom of the container. The remaining liquid is then drawn off for use as a stock solution.

Stone tanks can also be sterilized by scrubbing the sides and bottom thoroughly with solid calcium hypochlorite to which enough water has been added to form a paste. The tank should then be rinsed thoroughly (five or six times) with clear water.

CHAPTER X

FORMULAS

It is best to use formulas that are recommended by the manufacturers for their products; they are adjusted to the materials concerned and give better results than others.

Formulas for most all types of photographic work are included in this chapter. The times of development published with each developer are only intended to serve as a guide to the user because it is realized that individual conditions of use vary somewhat. Furthermore, the time of development for either tray or tank will vary according to the subject photographed, the sensitive material used, and the degree of contrast required. Greater or less contrast may be obtained with any developer by developing for longer or shorter times than those specified.

Several different alkalies are used in compounding the Eastman formulas according to the degree of contrast desired. Sodium carbonate, desiccated, is specified in many formulas. If monohydrated sodium carbonate is used, the quantity given in the formula must be increased 17 per cent. All regular developer formulas containing the alkali, *Kodalk*, are designated by the letters "DK" before the formula number.

DEVELOPERS for FILMS and PLATES

The following formulas (D-61a and DK-50) represent satisfactory developers for general use with films and plates. When kept up to normal volume by the addition of replenisher, both formulas will give good results over a period of one to two months. Formula DK-20 is recommended when finest grain is required.

When less contrast is desired, Formula D-76 is recommended. This may also be used for several weeks provided replenisher is added regularly.

The activity of D-76 may be increased by adding more borax or by substituting Kodalk for borax. Formula DK-60a is recommended for commercial photofinishing and for general use with high speed films and plates.

FORMULAS

Elon-Hydroquinone
For General Tray or Tank Use
[Formula D-61a]

Stock Solution

	Avoirdupois	Metric
Water (about 125° F.) (52° C.) . . .	16 ounces	500.0 cc.
Elon	45 grains	3.1 grams
Sodium Sulfite, desiccated (E.K.Co.) .	3 ounces	90.0 grams
Sodium Bisulfite (E.K.Co.)	30 grains	2.1 grams
Hydroquinone	85 grains	5.9 grams
Sodium Carbonate, desiccated (E.K.Co.)	165 grains	11.5 grams
Potassium Bromide	24 grains	1.7 grams
Cold water to make	32 ounces	1.0 liter

Dissolve chemicals in the order given.

For *tray* use take one part of stock solution to one part of water. Develop for about 7 minutes at 65° F. (18° C.).

For *tank* use take one part of stock solution and 3 parts of water. At a temperature of 65° F. (18° C.), the development time is about 14 minutes. It is advisable to make up a greater quantity than is needed to fill the tank. If the developer in the tank is of normal strength, but the volume of solution has been reduced, add a sufficient quantity of the surplus stock solution (diluted 1:3) to fill the tank.

If the strength of the solution, as well as the volume, has been reduced, add a sufficient quantity of the replenisher (Formula D-61R) to adjust the development time satisfactorily.

Replenisher Solution
For Formula D-61a
[Formula D-61R]

Stock Solution A

	Avoirdupois	Metric
Water (about 125° F.) (52° C.) . . .	96 ounces	3.0 liters
Elon	85 grains	5.9 grams
Sodium Sulfite, desiccated (E.K.Co.) .	6 ounces	180.0 grams
Sodium Bisulfite (E.K.Co.)	55 grains	3.8 grams
Hydroquinone	170 grains	11.9 grams
Potassium Bromide	45 grains	3.1 grams
Cold water to make	1½ gallons	6.0 liters

Stock Solution B

Sodium Carbonate, desiccated (E.K.Co.)	8 ounces	240.0 grams
Water to make	64 ounces	2.0 liters

Dissolve chemicals in the order given.

For use take 3 parts of A and one part of B and add to the tank of developer as needed. Do not mix these solutions until ready to use.

[Formula DK-50] ***Kodalk Developer**
For Professional Films and Plates

	Avoirdupois	Metric
Water (about 125° F.) (52° C.)	64 ounces	500.0 cc.
Elon	145 grains	2.5 grams
Sodium Sulfite, desiccated (E.K.Co.)	4 ounces	30.0 grams
Hydroquinone	145 grains	2.5 grams
Kodalk	1 oz. 145 grains	10.0 grams
Potassium Bromide	29 grains	0.5 gram
Water to make	1 gallon	1.0 liter

Dissolve chemicals in the order given.

*By increasing or decreasing the quantity of Kodalk in any developer containing this chemical, it is possible (a) to increase or decrease the contrast obtained in a given time of development, or (b) to decrease or increase the time of development without affecting the contrast.

Use without dilution for average contrast for commercial photography. Develop about 10 minutes at 65° F. (18° C.) in a tank of fresh developer.

For portraiture or where less contrast is desired, take one part stock solution and one part water. Develop about 9 minutes at 65° F. (18° C.) in a tank of fresh developer.

Formula DK-50 is recommended especially for the development of color separation negatives on Wratten Tricolor Panchromatic Plates.

Decrease the times given about 20 per cent for tray development.

Greater or less contrast can be obtained by developing for longer or shorter times than those specified.

[Formula DK-50R] **Replenisher**
For Formula DK-50

	Avoirdupois	Metric
Water (about 125° F.) (52° C.)	96 ounces	750.0 cc.
Elon	290 grains	5.0 grams
Sodium Sulfite, desiccated (E.K.Co.)	4 ounces	30.0 grams
Hydroquinone	1 oz. 145 grains	10.0 grams
Kodalk	5¼ ounces	40.0 grams
Water to make	1 gallon	1.0 liter

Dissolve chemicals in the order given.

Add to the tank as needed to maintain the level of the solution. If the developer stock solution is diluted 1:1, the replenisher should be diluted in the same proportion. If the quantity of Kodalk is increased in DK-50 over that in the regular formula, it may be necessary in some cases to discard some of the used developer in order to maintain a constant development time.

Kodak Fine Grain Developer [Formula DK-20]
For use with Roll Films, Film Packs, Cut Films and Plates

	Avoirdupois	Metric
Water (about 125° F.) (52° C.)	96 ounces	750.0 cc.
Elon	290 grains	5.0 grams
Sodium Sulfite, desiccated (E.K.Co.)	13¼ ounces	100.0 grams
Kodalk	116 grains	2.0 grams
Sodium Thiocyanate (E.K.Co.)	58 grains	1.0 gram
Potassium Bromide	29 grains	0.5 gram
Cold water to make	1 gallon	1.0 liter

Dissolve chemicals in the order given.

Use without dilution.

Average time of development for roll film, film packs, cut films and plates is about 18 minutes in a tank of fresh developer at 65° F. (18° C.) or 14 minutes at 70° F. (21° C.).

For tray use, decrease the time about 20 per cent.

Increase or decrease the times for greater or less contrast.

Without replenishment, the time of development should be increased about 20 per cent for each roll (80 sq. in.) developed. Capacity about 6 rolls per 32 ounces (one liter) of developer.

Replenisher Solution [Formula DK-20R]
For use with Fine Grain Developer, Formula DK-20

	Avoirdupois	Metric
Water (about 125° F.) (52° C.)	96 ounces	750.0 cc.
Elon	1 ounce	7.5 grams
Sodium Sulfite, desiccated (E.K.Co.)	13¼ ounces	100.0 grams
Kodalk	2 ozs. 290 grains	20.0 grams
Sodium Thiocyanate (E.K.Co.)	290 grains	5.0 grams
Potassium Bromide	58 grains	1.0 gram
Cold water to make	1 gallon	1.0 liter

Dissolve chemicals in the order given.

Add the replenisher as required to maintain the volume of the solution. Capacity of DK-20 when replenished with DK-20R about 24 rolls per 32 ounces (one liter) of developer. Add about one oz. (30 cc.) for each roll processed.

Large Scale Use: A given highlight density will be maintained throughout the developer life for a constant development time at a constant temperature, provided the volume of replenisher added is about 6 gallons per 1000 rolls of film (80,000 square inches) processed.

94 ELEMENTARY PHOTOGRAPHIC CHEMISTRY

[Formula D-76] **Elon-Hydroquinone-Borax Developer**
For Greatest Shadow Detail on Panchromatic Materials

	Avoirdupois	Metric
Water (about 125° F.) (52° C.)	96 ounces	750.0 cc.
Elon	116 grains	2.0 grams
Sodium Sulfite, desiccated (E.K.Co.)	13¼ ounces	100.0 grams
Hydroquinone	290 grains	5.0 grams
Borax, granular (E.K.Co.)	116 grains	2.0 grams
Water to make	1 gallon	1.0 liter

Dissolve chemicals in the order given.

Use without dilution. For tank use, develop roll film, sheet film, and aero film about 20 minutes at 65° F. (18° C.) in the fresh developer; for tray use, decrease the time about 20%. Develop a longer or shorter time than that specified for more or less contrast.

A faster working developer can be obtained by increasing the quantity of borax. By increasing the borax quantity 10 times, from 116 grains to 2 oz. 290 grains per gallon (from 2 grams to 20 grams per liter), the development time will be about one-half that of regular D-76. If a still more active developer is required, replace the borax in D-76 with 10 times as much Kodalk (2 ozs. 290 grains of Kodalk per gallon) (20 grams per liter). With this concentration of Kodalk the development time will be one-quarter that of regular D-76.

Note: With use, Formula D-76 becomes slightly muddy, due to the formation of a suspension of colloidal silver and the tank usually becomes coated with a thin deposit of silver. Both these effects are harmless, however, and may be ignored.

[Formula D-76R] **Replenisher Solution**
For use with the Developer D-76

	Avoirdupois	Metric
Water (about 125° F.) (52° C.)	96 ounces	750.0 cc.
Elon	175 grains	3.0 grams
Sodium Sulfite, desiccated (E.K.Co.)	13¼ ounces	100.0 grams
Hydroquinone	1 ounce	7.5 grams
Borax, granular (E.K.Co.)	2 ozs. 290 grains	20.0 grams
Water to make	1 gallon	1.0 liter

Dissolve chemicals in the order given.

Use the replenisher without dilution and add to the tank to maintain the level of the solution.

Note: When Kodalk is substituted for borax in Formula D-76 and a replenisher is required, it is necessary to substitute Kodalk for borax in Formula D-76R as follows:

Kodalk Concentration in the Developer		Time of Tank Development	Kodalk Concentration in the Replenisher	
Per Liter	Per Gallon	65° F. (18° C.)	Per Liter	Per Gallon
2 grams	116 grains	20 min.	7.5 grams	1 ounce
5 grams	290 grains	10 min.	20.0 grams	2 oz. 290 grains
10 grams	1 oz. 145 grains	7½ min.	40.0 grams	5 oz. 145 grains
20 grams	2 oz. 290 grains	5 min.	*40.0 grams	*5 oz. 145 grains

*Discard some developer before adding replenisher.

FORMULAS

Elon-Pyro Developer [Formula D-7]
For General Portrait and Commercial Use

Stock Solution A

	Avoirdupois	Metric
Water (about 125° F.) (52° C.)	16 ounces	500.0 cc.
Elon	¼ ounce	7.5 grams
Sodium Bisulfite (E.K.Co.)	¼ ounce	7.5 grams
Pyro	1 ounce	30.0 grams
Potassium Bromide	60 grains	4.2 grams
Water to make	32 ounces	1.0 liter

Stock Solution B

	Avoirdupois	Metric
Water	32 ounces	1.0 liter
Sodium Sulfite, desiccated (E.K.Co.)	5 ounces	150.0 grams

Stock Solution C

	Avoirdupois	Metric
Water	32 ounces	1.0 liter
Sodium Carbonate, desiccated (E.K.Co.)	2½ ounces	75.0 grams

Dissolve chemicals in the order given.

For Tray Development—

Take one part of A, one part of B, one part of C and 8 parts of water. Develop about 8 minutes at 65° F. (18° C.).

For Tank Development—

Take one part of A, one part of B, one part of C and 13 parts of water. Develop about 11 minutes at 65° F. (18° C.).

This developer can be used for two or three weeks if the volume is maintained by adding fresh developer in the proportion of one part each of A, B, and C to 4 parts of water. It is usually necessary to increase the development time as the developer ages.

Three-Solution Pyro [Formula D-1]
For Tray or Tank Use

Stock Solution A

	Avoirdupois	Metric
Sodium Bisulfite (E.K.Co.)	140 grains	9.8 grams
Pyro	2 ounces	60.0 grams
Potassium Bromide	16 grains	1.1 grams
Water to make	32 ounces	1.0 liter

Stock Solution B

	Avoirdupois	Metric
Water	32 ounces	1.0 liter
Sodium Sulfite, desiccated (E.K.Co.)	3½ ounces	105.0 grams

Stock Solution C

	Avoirdupois	Metric
Water	32 ounces	1.0 liter
Sodium Carbonate, desiccated (E.K.Co.)	2½ ounces	75.0 grams

Dissolve chemicals in the order given.

(Over)

For Tray Development—
Take one part of A, one part of B, one part of C, and 7 parts of water. Develop about 6 minutes at 65° F. (18° C.).

For Tank Development—
Take one part of A, one part of B, one part of C, and 11 parts of water. Develop about 12 minutes at 65° F. (18° C.).

Because of its rapid rate of oxidation and staining tendency, this developer should be discarded at once after use.

[Formula D-90] **Two-Solution Pyro Tray Developer**

Stock Solution A

	Avoirdupois	Metric
Sodium Sulfite, desiccated (E.K.Co.)	2 ozs. 145 grains	70.0 grams
Sodium Bisulfite (E.K.Co.)	245 grains	17.0 grams
Pyro	290 grains	20.0 grams
Water to make	32 ounces	1.0 liter

Stock Solution B

	Avoirdupois	Metric
Sodium Carbonate, desiccated (E.K.Co.)	2½ ounces	75.0 grams
Potassium Bromide	15 grains	1.0 gram
Water to make	32 ounces	1.0 liter

Dissolve chemicals in the order given.

For average use take one part of Stock Solution A, one part of Stock Solution B, and 2 parts of water. Develop about 5 minutes at 65° F. (18° C.). For greater contrast, use one part of A, one part of B, and one part of water; for less contrast, use one part of A, one part of B, and 4 parts of water.

[Formula D-72] **Elon-Hydroquinone Developer**
For Development of Fast Orthochromatic and Panchromatic Films and Plates for Press Photography

Stock Solution

	Avoirdupois	Metric
Water (about 125° F.) (52° C.)	16 ounces	500.0 cc.
Elon	45 grains	3.1 grams
Sodium Sulfite, desiccated (E.K.Co.)	1½ ounces	45.0 grams
Hydroquinone	175 grains	12.0 grams
Sodium Carbonate, desiccated (E.K.Co)	2¼ ounces	67.5 grams
Potassium Bromide	27 grains	1.9 grams
Water to make	32 ounces	1.0 liter

Dissolve chemicals in the order given.

For general use: Take one part of stock solution to one part of water. Develop for 3 to 5 minutes in a tank or 2½ to 4 minutes in a tray at 65° F. (18° C.) according to the contrast desired. For less contrast, dilute 1 : 2; for greater contrast, use without dilution.

FORMULAS

Maximum Energy Developer
For High Speed Films or Plates
[Formula D-82]

	Avoirdupois	Metric
Water (about 125° F.) (52° C.)	24 ounces	750.0 cc.
Wood Alcohol	1½ ounces	48.0 cc.
Elon	200 grains	14.0 grams
Sodium Sulfite, desiccated (E.K.Co.)	1¾ ounces	52.5 grams
Hydroquinone	200 grains	14.0 grams
Sodium Hydroxide (Caustic Soda) (E.K.Co.)	125 grains	8.8 grams
Potassium Bromide	125 grains	8.8 grams
Cold water to make	32 ounces	1.0 liter

Dissolve chemicals in the order given.

Develop about 3 to 5 minutes at 65° F. (18° C.) in a tray of fresh developer according to the contrast desired and the amount of fog which can be tolerated.

The prepared developer does not keep more than a few days. If wood alcohol is not added and the developer is diluted, the solution is not so active as in the concentrated form. This developer gives the greatest possible density with negatives having a minimum exposure.

Pyro Tray Developer
For Display Transparencies, Copy Negatives and Ciné Enlargements
[Formula D-84]

Stock Solution A

	Avoirdupois	Metric
Water	24 ounces	750.0 cc.
Sodium Sulfite, desiccated (E.K.Co.)	6 ounces	180.0 grams
Pyro	1 ounce	30.0 grams
Water to make	32 ounces	1.0 liter

Stock Solution B

Water	32 ounces	1.0 liter
Sodium Carbonate, desiccated (E.K.Co.)	4 ounces	120.0 grams
Potassium Bromide	55 grains	3.8 grams

Dissolve chemicals in the order given.

For use, take one part A, one part B, and 4 parts water. Develop about 4 minutes at 65° F. (18° C.).

Kodelon-Hydroquinone-Kodalk Developer
For General Use with Films and Plates
[Formula DK-93]

	Avoirdupois	Metric
Water (about 125° F.) (52° C.)	64 ounces	500.0 cc.
Kodelon	290 grains	5.0 grams
Sodium Sulfite, desiccated (E.K.Co.)	4 ounces	30.0 grams
Hydroquinone	145 grains	2.5 grams
Kodalk	2 ozs. 290 grains	20.0 grams
Potassium Bromide	28 grains	0.5 gram
Cold water to make	1 gallon	1.0 liter

Dissolve chemicals in the order given.

(Over)

Use without dilution. Develop roll films about 10 minutes in a tank of fresh developer at 65° F. (18° C.).

Develop professional films and plates about 8 minutes in a tank at 65° F. (18° C.).

Greater or less contrast may be obtained by developing longer or shorter times than those specified.

The use of Formula DK-93 is especially recommended for those persons subject to trouble from skin irritation.

[Formula DK-60a]   *Kodalk Developer
For Tray, Deep Tank and Machine Development of Roll Films, Film Packs, Sheet Films and Plates

	Avoirdupois	Metric
Water (about 125° F.) (52° C.)	5 gallons	750.0 cc.
Elon	3¼ ounces	2.5 grams
Sodium Sulfite, desiccated (E.K.Co.)	4 lb. 2½ ounces	50.0 grams
Hydroquinone	3¼ ounces	2.5 grams
Kodalk	1 lb. 10¾ ounces	20.0 grams
Potassium Bromide	290 grains	0.5 gram
Water to make	10 gallons	1.0 liter

Dissolve chemicals in the order given.

Develop roll films *about 9 minutes at 65° F. (18° C.) or 7 minutes at 70° F. (21° C.) in a tank of fresh developer.

Develop Verichrome film packs for about 20 per cent longer than Verichrome roll film; develop other Kodak film packs for the same time as the corresponding Kodak roll films.

Tray development for all films and film packs should be about 20 per cent less than tank development times.

Develop sheet films and plates about 8 minutes in a tank of fresh developer at 65° F. (18° C.).

Increase or decrease the times for greater or less contrast.

*Note: For maximum emulsion speed, develop Kodak 35 mm. Super-XX Panchromatic Film and Bantam Super-XX Panchromatic Film about 12 minutes at 65° F. (18° C.) or 9½ minutes at 70° F. (21° C.) in a tank of fresh developer.

[Formula DK-60aTR]   Replenisher
Replenisher for DK-60a for Tank Development

	Avoirdupois	Metric
Water (about 125° F.) (52° C.)	96 ounces	750.0 cc.
Elon	290 grains	5.0 grams
Sodium Sulfite, desiccated (E.K.Co.)	6 oz. 290 grains	50.0 grams
Hydroquinone	1 oz. 145 grains	10.0 grams
Kodalk	5 oz. 145 grains	40.0 grams
Cold water to make	1 gallon	1.0 liter

Dissolve the chemicals in the order given.

(*Continued on next page*)

Add the replenisher as required to maintain the liquid level in the developer tank. With deep tanks, 38 or 48 gallon, the replenisher should be added before the liquid level has dropped 2 inches.

The development time will be maintained approximately constant at a given temperature, provided 8 gallons of replenisher are added per 1000 rolls of film processed (80 sq. in. = one roll).

Automatic Machine Processing: For automatic machine processing, when less developer is carried out of the tank by the film than with hand processing, the prepared package replenisher, Formula DK-60aMR for machine development should be used.

The development time will be maintained approximately constant at a given temperature provided 6 gallons of DK-60aMR are added per 1000 rolls of film processed.

Tropical Development

For best results it is advisable to have the temperature of the solutions as near 65° F. (18° C.) as possible. There are times, however, when it is impossible to do this owing to unusual conditions. This is especially true in tropical countries where the temperatures are high and where it is difficult to obtain fresh, cool water.

To develop films at temperatures up to 90° F. (32° C.) Kodalk Developer, Formula DK-15, is especially recommended. This formula has the following advantages: (1) It is non-blistering because no gas is formed when the developer is added to the acid hardening bath or the acid fixing bath. (2) The development rate changes slowly with time so that on slight overdevelopment the negatives will not be too dense. (3) It has a minimum scumming tendency in conjunction with the average acid fixing bath.

Kodalk Tropical Developer [Formula DK-15]
(Non-blistering)

	Avoirdupois	Metric
Water (about 125° F.) (52° C.)	24 ounces	750.0 cc.
Elon	82 grains	5.7 grams
Sodium Sulfite, desiccated (E.K.Co.)	3 ounces	90.0 grams
Kodalk	¾ ounce	22.5 grams
Potassium Bromide	27 grains	1.9 grams
*Sodium Sulfate, desiccated	1½ ounces	45.0 grams
Cold water to make	32 ounces	1.0 liter

*If it is desired to use crystalline sodium sulfate instead of the desiccated sulfate, then 3½ ounces per 32 ounces (105 grams per liter) should be used.

Dissolve chemicals in the order given.

(Over)

Average time for tank development is 9 to 12 minutes at 65° F. (18° C.) and 2 to 3 minutes at 90° F. (32° C.), in the fresh developer according to the contrast desired. When working *below* 75° F. (24° C.) the sulfate may be omitted if a more rapid formula is required. Development time *without* the sulfate is 5 to 7 minutes at 65° F. (18° C.). Develop about 20 per cent less for tray use.

When development is completed rinse the film or plate in water for one or 2 seconds only and immerse in the Tropical Hardener (Formula SB-4, page 114) for 3 minutes (omit water rinse if film tends to soften); then fix for at least 10 minutes in an acid hardening fixing bath, such as Formula F-5, page 115, and wash for 10 to 15 minutes in water (not over 95° F.) (35° C.).

Further details on tropical development will be found in the booklet "Tropical Development" obtainable on request from the Eastman Kodak Company, Rochester, N. Y.

A tropical developer for process work, Formula D-13, will be found on page 103.

[Formula D-91]   **Kodelon Tropical Developer**

	Avoirdupois	Metric
Water (about 125° F.) (52° C.)	24 ounces	750.0 cc.
Kodelon	100 grains	7.0 grams
Sodium Sulfite, desiccated (E.K.Co.)	1 oz. 290 grains	50.0 grams
Sodium Carbonate, desiccated (E.K.Co.)	1 oz. 290 grains	50.0 grams
Water to make	32 ounces	1.0 liter

Dissolve chemicals in the order given.

Average time of development, 7 to 9 minutes at 65° F. (18° C.) and 2 to 3 minutes at 90° F. (32° C.) in the fresh developer according to the contrast desired. When using D-91 above 80° F. (26.5° C.) best results will be obtained by adding 5 to 10 per cent sodium sulfate (desiccated) to the developer. In one quart, a concentration of 5% would be obtained if 1¾ oz. of sulfate, desiccated, are used (50 grams to one liter). Rinse, harden, fix, and wash as recommended following Formula DK-15, above.

Process Developers

The following Hydroquinone-Caustic Process Developers, Formulas D-8 and D-9, will give very high density and will be found best for line work. Formula D-8 has somewhat better keeping properties in an open tray than D-9 and gives slightly higher density in a shorter time of development.

Both formulas D-8 and D-9 should be used at a temperature of 65° F. (18° C.), not warmer, and should never be used colder than 55° F. (13° C.).

The Elon-Hydroquinone Process Developer, Formula D-11, keeps better than D-8 or D-9 but it will not produce as high density.

Single Solution Hydroquinone-Caustic Developer [Formula D-8]

For Maximum Contrast on Process and Panchromatic Process Films and Plates, and Kodalith Stripping Film (Superspeed)

Stock Solution

	Avoirdupois	Metric
Water	96 ounces	750.0 cc.
Sodium Sulfite, desiccated (E.K.Co.)	12 ounces	90.0 grams
Hydroquinone	6 ounces	45.0 grams
*Sodium Hydroxide (Caustic Soda) (E.K.Co.)	5 ounces	37.5 grams
Potassium Bromide	4 ounces	30.0 grams
Water to make	1 gallon	1.0 liter

Dissolve chemicals in the order given. Stir the solution thoroughly before use.

For use, take 2 parts of stock solution and one part of water. Develop about 2 minutes in a tray at 65° F. (18° C.). This formula is especially recommended for making line and halftone screen negatives for printing directly on metal.

Develop Kodalith Stripping Film (Superspeed) about 2 minutes at 65° F. (18° C.) in the diluted developer (2 parts stock solution to one part water). After development, rinse in the Acetic Acid Rinse Bath (Formula SB-1a, page 114) for 5 seconds, fix for 1½ minutes in the F-5 fixing bath (page 115), and wash for 2 to 3 minutes at 80° F. (26° C.), when the skin will have loosened sufficiently to permit its being stripped from the paper support.

For general use, a formula which is slightly less alkaline and gives almost as much density can be obtained by using 3¾ ounces of sodium hydroxide per gallon of stock solution (28 grams per liter) instead of the quantity given in the formula.

[Formula D-9] **Process Tray Developer**
Hydroquinone-Caustic Soda

Stock Solution A

	Avoirdupois	Metric
Water (about 125° F.) (52° C.)	16 ounces	500.0 cc.
Sodium Bisulfite (E.K.Co.)	¾ ounce	22.5 grams
Hydroquinone	¾ ounce	22.5 grams
Potassium Bromide	¾ ounce	22.5 grams
Cold water to make	32 ounces	1.0 liter

Stock Solution B

	Avoirdupois	Metric
Cold water	32 ounces	1.0 liter
*Sodium Hydroxide (Caustic Soda) (E.K.Co.)	1¾ ounces	52.5 grams

*See caution note below on handling sodium hydroxide.

Dissolve chemicals in the order given.

Use equal parts of A and B and develop not more than two minutes at 65° F. (18° C.). Wash *thoroughly* after development and before fixing, otherwise stains and dichroic fog will result. Development slows up greatly below 55° F. (13° C.).

Caution: Cold water should always be used when dissolving sodium hydroxide (caustic soda) because considerable heat is evolved. If hot water is used, the solution will boil with explosive violence and may cause serious burns if the hot alkali spatters on the hands or face. Solution A should be stirred thoroughly when the caustic alkali is added to it; otherwise the heavy caustic solution will sink to the bottom.

[Formula D-11] **Process Tank or Tray Developer**
Elon-Hydroquinone

	Avoirdupois	Metric
Water (about 125° F.) (52° C.)	16 ounces	500.0 cc.
Elon	15 grains	1.0 gram
Sodium Sulfite, desiccated (E.K.Co.)	2½ ounces	75.0 grams
Hydroquinone	130 grains	9.0 grams
Sodium Carbonate, desiccated (E.K.Co.)	365 grains	25.0 grams
Potassium Bromide	73 grains	5.0 grams
Cold water to make	32 ounces	1.0 liter

Dissolve chemicals in the order given.

Formula D-11 used at 65° F. (18° C.), in either tank or tray will give very good contrast in 5 minutes. The developer is recommended for use with Process and Process Panchromatic Films or Plates, for general commercial photography and for making half-tone screen negatives from which positive transparencies are to be made for dot etching.

(Continued on next page)

FORMULAS 103

When less contrast is desired, the developer should be diluted with an equal volume of water.

For line drawings on lantern slides, use without dilution and develop about 5 minutes in a tray or 6 minutes in a tank at 65° F. (18° C.).

A brief treatment with dilute Farmer's Reducer (Formula R-4, page 123) after fixing and washing will give added brilliance to the slide.

Tropical Process Developer [Formula D-13]
Kodelon-Hydroquinone

	Avoirdupois	Metric
Water (about 125° F.) (52° C.)	24 ounces	750.0 cc.
Kodelon	75 grains	5.1 grams
Sodium Sulfite, desiccated (E.K.Co.)	1¾ ounces	52.5 grams
Hydroquinone	150 grains	10.5 grams
Sodium Carbonate, desiccated (E.K.Co.)	1¾ ounces	52.5 grams
Potassium Iodide	30 grains	2.1 grams
*Sodium Sulfate, desiccated	1½ ounces	45.0 grams
Water to make	32 ounces	1.0 liter

*If it is preferred to use sodium sulfate crystals, instead of the desiccated sulfate then use 3½ ounces per 32 ounces (105 grams per liter.)

Dissolve chemicals in the order given.

Use without dilution. Develop about 6 minutes at 85° F. (29° C.), or for proportionately longer times at lower temperatures. Rinse for 30 seconds and immerse for 3 minutes in a 5% formalin solution. Then wash for one minute, fix in an acid hardening fixing bath (Formula F-5, page 115) and wash about 15 minutes in fresh running water.

Kodalith Film, Plate and Paper Developer [Formula D-85]
For Line or Half-tone Negatives of Extreme Contrast

	Avoirdupois	Metric
Water (about 90° F.) (32° C.)	64 ounces	500.0 cc.
Sodium Sulfite, desiccated (E.K.Co.)	4 ounces	30.0 grams
Paraformaldehyde (E.K.Co.)	1 ounce	7.5 grams
Potassium Metabisulfite	150 grains	2.6 grams
*Boric Acid, Crystals	1 ounce	7.5 grams
Hydroquinone	3 ounces	22.5 grams
Potassium Bromide	90 grains	1.6 grams
Water to make	1 gallon	1.0 liter

*Use crystalline boric acid as specified. Powdered boric acid dissolves with great difficulty and its use should be avoided.

Dissolve chemicals in the order given.

Mixing Directions: Dissolve the chemicals in water which half fills a narrow mouthed bottle. After adding each chemical, place the stopper in the bottle so that only a small

(*Over*)

quantity of air is present during agitation. When all the chemicals have been dissolved, add cold water until the solution reaches the position occupied by the stopper. Insert the stopper tightly to exclude the air. Allow the developer to stand about two hours after mixing.

Before pouring into the tray, the solution should be cooled in the bottle to 65° F. (18° C.). If only a portion of the contents of the bottle are used at one time, it is suggested that the balance be saved by filling a bottle of smaller size which should then be stoppered tightly.

Time of Development: For line negatives, 1½ to 2 minutes at 65° F. (18° C.); for half-tone negatives, not over 2½ minutes at 65° F. (18° C.). With a correctly timed exposure, the image should appear in 30 to 45 seconds at the temperature specified.

The life of the developer will be prolonged if the temperature does not rise above 70° F. (21° C.) during use.

This developer has the property of cutting off development very sharply in the low densities thus insuring clear dot formation in half-tone negatives.

The following two-solution formula has better keeping qualities than D-85 and is recommended when a small volume of solution is required for occasional use.

[Formula D-85b] **Kodalith Film, Plate and Paper Developer**
For Line or Half-tone Negatives
of Extreme Contrast

Stock Solution A

	Avoirdupois	Metric
Water (about 125° F.) (52° C.)	64 ounces	2.0 liters
Sodium Sulfite, desiccated (E.K.Co.)	4 ounces	120.0 grams
*Boric Acid, crystals	1 ounce	30.0 grams
Hydroquinone	3 ounces	90.0 grams
Potassium Bromide	90 grains	6.3 grams
Cold water to make	96 ounces	3.0 liters

*Use crystalline boric acid as specified; powdered boric acid dissolves with great difficulty, and its use should be avoided.

Stock Solution B
(Keep in a well-stoppered brown bottle)

Water (about 90° F.) (32° C.)	24 ounces	750.0 cc.
Potassium Metabisulfite	150 grains	10.5 grams
Sodium Sulfite, desiccated (E.K.Co.)	15 grains	1.0 gram
Paraformaldehyde (E.K.Co.)	1 ounce	30.0 grams
*Phenosafranine (1:1000 solution)	5 drams	20.0 cc.
Cold water to make	32 ounces	1.0 liter

*To prepare a 1:1000 solution, dissolve 15 grains (one gram) of phenosafranine in 32 ounces (one liter) of distilled water at 125° F. (52° C.). Allow to cool before use.

Dissolve chemicals in the order given.

(Continued on next page)

FORMULAS

For use: Add one part of Stock Solution B to 3 parts of Stock Solution A. Develop by inspection for 1½ to 2 minutes at 65° F. (18° C.) for line negatives or not over 2½ minutes at 65° F. (18° C.) for half-tone negatives. With correct exposures the image should flash up in about 30 to 45 seconds.

Follow the instructions for use given with Formula D-85.

Formulas for Motion Picture Film

Elon-Hydroquinone-Borax Developer [Formula D-76]
For Panchromatic Negatives and Variable Density Sound Negatives

	Avoirdupois	Metric
Elon	2 pounds	2.0 grams
Sodium Sulfite, desiccated (E.K.Co.)	100 pounds	100.0 grams
Hydroquinone	5 pounds	5.0 grams
Borax, granular (E.K.Co.)	2 pounds	2.0 grams
Water to make	120 gallons	1.0 liter

Directions for Mixing: Dissolve the Elon separately in a small volume of water (at about 125° F.) (52° C.) and add the solution to the tank. Then dissolve approximately one-quarter of the sulfite separately in hot water (at about 160° F.) (71° C.), add the hydroquinone with stirring until completely dissolved. Then add this solution to the tank. Now dissolve the remainder of the sulfite in hot water (about 160° F.) (71° C.), add the borax and when dissolved, pour the entire solution into the tank and dilute to the required volume with cold water.

Average development time is 8 to 12 minutes at 65° F. (18° C.) in the fresh developer according to the contrast desired. The developer tank usually becomes coated with a thin white deposit of silver, but this will do no harm. The developer may become slightly muddy due to the formation of a suspension of colloidal silver, but it is harmless and can be ignored.

For Duplicate Negatives: Average time of development is 6 to 9 minutes at 65° F. (18° C.), according to the contrast desired.

Replenishment: The replenisher formula given on page 94 for small tank use is also satisfactory for motion picture development. The information given on page 94 on methods of increasing the activity of D-76 applies equally well to large scale processing.

106 ELEMENTARY PHOTOGRAPHIC CHEMISTRY

[Formula D-76d] **Buffered Borax Negative Developer**

	Avoirdupois	Metric
Elon	2 pounds	2.0 grams
Sodium Sulfite, desiccated (E.K.Co.)	100 pounds	100.0 grams
Hydroquinone	5 pounds	5.0 grams
Borax, granular (E.K.Co.)	8 pounds	8.0 grams
*Boric Acid, crystals	8 pounds	8.0 grams
Water to make	120 gallons	1.0 liter

*Crystalline boric acid should be used. Powdered boric acid dissolves only with great difficulty, and its use should be avoided.

Directions for mixing: Follow the same directions as given for Formula D-76, pages 94 and 105.

With a ratio of equal parts of borax and boric acid as given above, the rate of development is unchanged from that of D-76. By increasing the quantity of borax with a corresponding decrease in the boric acid content, the development rate is increased. By decreasing the borax and increasing the boric acid proportionately, the development rate is decreased.

Developers with a high concentration of boric acid have a shorter useful life because the reduction potential of the developing agents is lowered. They are also more susceptible to the reaction products of development.

[Formula D-78] **Athenon (Glycin) Negative Developer**
Reel or Tank

	Avoirdupois	Metric
Water	80 gallons	750.0 cc.
Sodium Sulfite, desiccated (E.K.Co.)	3 pounds	3.0 grams
Athenon (Glycin)	3 pounds	3.0 grams
Sodium Carbonate, desiccated (E.K.Co.)	6 pounds	6.0 grams
Water to make	120 gallons	1.0 liter

Dissolve chemicals in the order given.

Time of development: 15 to 25 minutes at 65° F. (18° C.) according to the contrast desired.

[Formula D-79] **Pyro Tank Developer**
For Negative Motion Picture Film

	Avoirdupois	Metric
Water	80 gallons	750.0 cc.
Sodium Sulfite, desiccated (E.K.Co.)	25 pounds	25.0 grams
Pyro	2½ pounds	2.5 grams
Sodium Carbonate, desiccated (E.K.Co.)	5 pounds	5.0 grams
Potassium Bromide	8 ounces	0.5 gram
Water to make	120 gallons	1.0 liter

Dissolve chemicals in the order given.

Time of development: 9 to 12 minutes at 65° F. (18° C.) according to the contrast desired.

FORMULAS

Normal Positive Tank Developer [Formula D-16]
Also for Variable Width Sound Negatives

	Avoirdupois	Metric
Water (about 125° F.) (52° C.)	80 gallons	750.0 cc.
Elon	5 ounces	0.31 gram
Sodium Sulfite, desiccated (E.K.Co.)	39½ pounds	39.6 grams
Hydroquinone	6 pounds	6.0 grams
Sodium Carbonate, desiccated (E.K.Co.)	18¾ pounds	18.7 grams
Potassium Bromide	13¾ ounces	0.86 gram
Citric Acid	11 ounces	0.68 gram
Potassium Metabisulfite	1½ pounds	1.5 grams
Cold water to make	120 gallons	1.0 liter

Dissolve chemicals in the order given.

Time of development: 5 to 10 minutes at 65° F. (18° C.) according to the contrast desired.

Replenisher for Formula D-16 [Formula D-16R]

	Avoirdupois	Metric
Water (about 125° F.) (52° C.)	80 gallons	750.0 cc.
Elon	4 ozs. 350 grains	0.3 gram
Sodium Sulfite, desiccated (E.K.Co.)	40 pounds	40.0 grams
Hydroquinone	9 pounds	9.0 grams
Sodium Carbonate, desiccated (E.K.Co.)	38 pounds	38.0 grams
Citric Acid	11¼ ounces	0.7 gram
Potassium Metabisulfite	1½ pounds	1.5 grams
Water to make	120 gallons	1.0 liter

Dissolve chemicals in the order given.

Add to the tank as needed to make up for the developer carried out by the film. When added in this manner, the developer activity will be maintained approximately constant with respect to positive film.

Formulas for Special Work

Kodalk Aero Film Developer [Formula DK-60b]

	Avoirdupois	Metric
Water (about 125° F.) (52° C.)	96 ounces	750.0 cc.
Elon	73 grains	1.25 grams
Sodium Sulfite, desiccated (E.K.Co.)	3 ozs. 145 grains	25.0 grams
Hydroquinone	73 grains	1.25 grams
Kodalk	1 oz. 145 grains	10.0 grams
Sodium Sulfate, desiccated	6 ozs. 290 grains	50.0 grams
*Benzotriazole (E.K.Co.) (0.2% Stock Solution)	1 fluid oz.	8.0 cc.
Potassium Bromide	15 grains	0.25 gram
Water to make	1 gallon	1.0 liter

*A 0.2% Stock Solution of Benzotriazole may be made by dissolving 15 grains of this chemical in 16 ounces of water, about 125° F. (one gram in 500 cc. at 52° C.) Cool the Stock Solution before use.

Dissolve the chemicals in the order given.

(Over)

Use without dilution. Develop in a tank of fresh developer about 25 minutes for average contrast, or 15 minutes for low contrast at 70° F. (21° C.).

When negatives of higher contrast are desired, develop in Formula D-19; for low contrast, use Formula D-76, page 94.

[Formula D-87] **Pyro Developer for Aero Film**

	Avoirdupois	Metric
Sodium Sulfite, desiccated (E.K.Co.)	1 oz. 60 grains	8.6 grams
Sodium Carbonate, desiccated (E.K.Co.)	1 oz. 125 grains	9.6 grams
Potassium Bromide	73 grains	1.25 grams
Potassium Metabisulfite	57 grains	1.0 gram
Pyro	165 grains	2.9 grams
Water to make	1 gallon	1.0 liter

Dissolve chemicals in the order given.

This developer oxidizes rapidly so that the pyro should be added just before use. Dissolve the sulfite, carbonate, and bromide, and add to the tank. Dissolve the metabisulfite separately in a small volume of water and then add the pyro. When ready to develop, add the pyro-metabisulfite solution to the tank and make up to volume with water.

Develop for 30 minutes at 65° F. (18° C.).

Note: Because of the comparatively short keeping properties of this developer, it is desirable to use a fresh solution when developing each roll of film.

[Formula D-19] **High Contrast Developer**
Eastman Aero Films, Press Films and Plates, and for Wratten "M," Metallographic, Eastman Spectroscopic and Infra-red Sensitive Plates

Stock Solution

	Avoirdupois	Metric
Water (about 125° F.) (52° C.)	64 ounces	500.0 cc.
Elon	128 grains	2.2 grams
Sodium Sulfite, desiccated (E.K.Co.)	12 ozs. 360 grains	96.0 grams
Hydroquinone	1 oz. 75 grains	8.8 grams
Sodium Carbonate, desiccated (E.K.Co.)	6 ozs. 180 grains	48.0 grams
Potassium Bromide	290 grains	5.0 grams
Cold water to make	1 gallon	1.0 liter

Dissolve chemicals in order given.

Use without dilution for Aero films. Develop about 15 minutes in a tank of fresh developer at 65° F. (18° C.). Decrease the development time about ½ minute for each degree rise in temperature (Fahrenheit). When less contrast is desired, use Formula D-76 as recommended on page 94.

(*Continued on next page*)

FORMULAS

For Press films and plates, use without dilution and develop about 5 minutes at 65° F. (18° C.) or 4 minutes at 70° F. (21° C.) in a tray of fresh developer.

For Wratten "M" and Metallographic Plates, use without dilution. For high contrast, develop about 3½ minutes, and for extreme contrast, about 6 minutes, at 65° F. (18° C.) in a tray of fresh developer.

For Eastman Spectroscopic Plates, use without dilution, and develop about 5 minutes in a tray at 65° F. (18° C.).

For Eastman Infra-red Sensitive Plates, take one part Stock Solution and 4 parts water and develop about 5 minutes in a tray or 6½ minutes in a tank at 65° F. (18° C.).

Use the F-10 Fixing Bath (page 117) with D-19 developer for best results.

Low and Normal Contrast Developer [Formula D-76c]
For Wratten "M" and Metallographic Plates

	Avoirdupois	Metric
Water (about 125° F.) (52° C.)	96 ounces	750.0 cc.
Elon	116 grains	2.0 grams
Sodium Sulfite, desiccated (E.K.Co.)	13¼ ounces	100.0 grams
Hydroquinone	290 grains	5.0 grams
Borax, granular (E.K.Co.)	116 grains	2.0 grams
Potassium Iodide, 1% solution	1 dram	1.0 cc.
Potassium Bromide, 2.5% solution	10 drams	10.0 cc.
Cold water to make	1 gallon	1.0 liter

Dissolve chemicals in the order given.

Use without dilution.

For low contrast, develop about 5 minutes, and for normal contrast, about 6½ minutes, at 65° F. (18° C.) in a tray of fresh developer. Increase the time about 25% for tank development.

Autopositive Film Developer [Formula SD-12]
For Duplicating Negatives Directly from Original Negatives

	Avoirdupois	Metric
Water (about 125° F.) (52° C.)	16 ounces	500.0 cc.
Elon	15 grains	1.0 gram
Sodium Sulfite, desiccated (E.K.Co.)	1 oz. 145 grains	40.0 grams
Hydroquinone	45 grains	3.0 grams
Kodalk	1 oz. 145 grains	40.0 grams
Potassium Bromide	15 grains	1.0 gram
*Benzotriazole (E.K.Co.) (0.2% Stock Solution)	3¼ fluid oz.	100.0 cc.
Cold water to make	32 ounces	1.0 liter

*A 0.2% Stock Solution of Benzotriazole may be made by dissolving 15 grains of this chemical in 16 ounces of water, about 125° F. (one gram in 500 cc. of water at 52° C.). Cool the Stock Solution before use.

Dissolve chemicals in the order given.

(*Over*)

Develop about 5 minutes in a tray, or 6 minutes in a tank, at 65° F. (18° C.). After development, rinse in clear water or in an acetic acid rinse bath (SB-1), and fix in an acid hardening fixing bath, such as Eastman Formula F-5.

Important: Formula SD-12 is recommended for use only with Eastman Autopositive Commercial Safety Film.

Lantern Slide Developers

Formula D-72 is recommended for general use with lantern slide plates. It may be diluted in several ways to produce various degrees of contrast. (See page 111.)

Formula D-11 is recommended for slides of line drawings where very high density and contrast is required. (See pages 102-103.)

[Formula D-32]   **Warm Black Tones**

Stock Solution A

	Avoirdupois	Metric
Water (about 125° F.) (52° C.)	16 ounces	500.0 cc.
Sodium Sulfite, desiccated (E.K.Co.)	90 grains	6.3 grams
Hydroquinone	100 grains	7.0 grams
Potassium Bromide	50 grains	3.5 grams
Citric Acid	10 grains	0.7 gram
Cold water to make	32 ounces	1.0 liter

Stock Solution B

	Avoirdupois	Metric
Cold water	32 ounces	1.0 liter
Sodium Carbonate, desiccated (E.K.Co.)	1 ounce	30.0 grams
Sodium Hydroxide (Caustic Soda) (E.K.Co.)	60 grains	4.2 grams

Dissolve chemicals in the order given.

For use, take one part of A and one part of B. For still warmer tones, one part of A and 2 parts of B. Stir thoroughly before use.

Develop about 5 minutes at 70° F. (21° C.). See discussion on page 130 on the use of this formula.

DEVELOPERS FOR PAPERS

[Formula D-52]   **Portrait Paper Developer**

Stock Solution

	Avoirdupois	Metric
Water (about 125° F.) (52° C.)	16 ounces	500.0 cc.
Elon	22 grains	1.5 grams
Sodium Sulfite, desiccated (E.K.Co.)	¾ ounce	22.5 grams
Hydroquinone	90 grains	6.3 grams
Sodium Carbonate, desiccated (E.K.Co.)	½ ounce	15.0 grams
Cold water to make	32 ounces	1.0 liter

Dissolve chemicals in the order given.

(*Continued on next page*)

FORMULAS

For professional contact and projection papers such as Vitava Athena and Vitava Projection, use stock solution one part, water one part. To each 32 ounces (one liter) of this diluted developer, add ¼ ounce (8 cc.) of a 10% potassium bromide solution.

Develop not less than 1½ minutes at 70° F. (21° C.).

Note: More bromide may be added if warmer tones are desired.

Universal Paper Developer [Formula D-72]
For Amateur Contact Prints and Enlargements
Stock Solution

	Avoirdupois	Metric
Water (about 125° F.) (52° C.)	16 ounces	500.0 cc.
Elon	45 grains	3.1 grams
Sodium Sulfite, desiccated (E.K.Co.)	1½ ounces	45.0 grams
Hydroquinone	175 grains	12.0 grams
Sodium Carbonate, desiccated (E.K.Co.)	2¼ ounces	67.5 grams
Potassium Bromide	27 grains	1.9 grams
Cold water to make	32 ounces	1.0 liter

Dissolve chemicals in the order given.

For Chloride Papers such as Velox and Azo: Use stock solution one part, water 2 parts. Develop 45 seconds at 70° F. (21° C.).

For Bromide Papers: Use stock solution one part, water 4 parts. Develop not less than 1½ minutes at 70° F. (21° C.).

If greater contrast is desired with bromide papers use stock solution one part, water 2 parts; or stock solution one part, water one part. With the 1 : 1 dilution add 15 grains of potassium bromide per 32 ounces of developer (one gram per liter).

For Lantern Slides, take stock solution one part, water 2 parts. Develop one to 2 minutes at 70° F. (21° C.). For greater contrast, dilute 1 : 1 and for less contrast, dilute 1 : 4. For line drawings, Formula D-11 is recommended (see page 102). For warm tones, use Formula D-32, page 110.

Amidol Developer for Bromide Papers [Formula D-51]
Stock Solution

	Avoirdupois	Metric
Water (about 125° F.) (52° C.)	24 ounces	750.0 cc.
Sodium Sulfite, desiccated (E.K.Co.)	4 ounces	120.0 grams
Di-Aminophenol Hydrochloride (Amidol)	1¼ ounces	37.5 grams
Cold water to make	32 ounces	1.0 liter

Dissolve chemicals in the order given.

(Over)

For use, take 6 ozs. (180 cc.) Stock Solution, ¾ dram (3 cc.) 10% potassium bromide solution, and 24 ozs. (750 cc.) of water. This developer oxidizes rapidly when exposed to the air so that only a quantity sufficient for immediate use should be mixed. A blue-black tone is given by this developer with most bromide papers.

Direct Reversal Process on Paper
For Use with Eastman Super Speed Direct Positive Paper

The stages of the reversal printing process and the times required for each chemical treatment are as follows:

1. Exposure
2. Development (45 secs.—one min.)
3. Bleach (30 sec.)
4. Clearing (30 secs.)
5. Re-exposure
6. Re-development (30 secs.)
7. Fixation (if desired, but not necessary) (30 secs.)

It is necessary to wash the prints well in running water for at least 15 seconds between the different solutions. Where the recommended re-developer is used, it is necessary to expose the paper to artificial light or daylight before re-development. If convenient, the white light can be turned on as soon as the prints are placed in the clearing bath. If brown tones are desired, the sulfide re-developer may be used when it will be unnecessary to use white light.

[Formula D-88]   **First Developer**
                  For Direct Positive Prints

	Avoirdupois	Metric
Water (about 125° F.) (52° C.)	96 ounces	750.0 cc.
Sodium Sulfite, desiccated (E.K.Co.)	6½ ounces	48.8 grams
Hydroquinone	3¼ ounces	24.4 grams
*Boric Acid, crystals	¾ ounce	5.6 grams
Potassium Bromide	150 grains	2.6 grams
**Sodium Hydroxide (Caustic Soda) (E.K.Co.)	3¼ ounces	24.4 grams
Cold water to make	1 gallon	1.0 liter

*Use crystalline boric acid as specified. Powdered boric acid dissolves with great difficulty, and its use should be avoided.

**It is desirable to dissolve the caustic soda in a small volume of water in a separate container and then add it to the solution of the other constituents. Then dilute the whole to the required volume. If a glass container is employed in dissolving the caustic soda, the solution should be stirred constantly until the soda is dissolved to prevent cracking the glass container by the heat evolved.

Dissolve chemicals in the order given.
Use full strength at 70° F. (21° C.).

FORMULAS

Bleaching Bath [Formula R-9]

	Avoirdupois	Metric
Water	1 gallon	1.0 liter
Potassium Bichromate	1¼ ounces	9.4 grams
Sulfuric Acid, C.P. (E.K.Co.)	1½ fluid ozs.	12.0 cc.

Use full strength at 65° to 70° F. (18° to 21° C.). For more rapid bleaching, however, the quantities of acid and bichromate may be increased.

Clearing Bath [Formula CB-1]

	Avoirdupois	Metric
Sodium Sulfite, desiccated (E.K.Co.)	12 ounces	90.0 grams
Water to make	1 gallon	1.0 liter

Use full strength at 65° to 70° F. (18° to 21° C.).

Re-developer

A—Black-and-white prints.

Use first developer (Formula D-88) full strength at 65° to 70° F. (18° to 21° C.).

B—Sepia Tones.

If sepia tones are desired, use the following re-developer after clearing:

Sulfide Re-developer [Formula T-19]

	Avoirdupois	Metric
*Sodium Sulfide, fused (not sulfite)	300 grains	20.0 grams
Water to make	32 ounces	1.0 liter

*Use three times the quantity of crystalline sodium sulfide.

Use full strength at 65° to 70° F. (18° to 21° C.).

Fixing Bath

Prints of slightly greater brilliancy may be secured by fixing in the regular fixing bath (Formula F-1) after re-development in Formula D-88. It is important to wash for *at least 10 minutes* to insure removal of the fixing bath from the print. It is not necessary to use the fixing bath after the sulfide re-developer.

RINSE and HARDENING BATHS

[Formula SB-1] **Acid Rinse Bath for Papers**

After development, rinse prints thoroughly in running water or for at least 5 seconds in the following acid rinse bath before placing in the fixing bath (Formula F-1, page 119). For best results, use a fresh bath for each batch of prints.

	Avoirdupois	Metric
Water	32 ounces	1.0 liter
*Acetic Acid (28% pure) (E.K.Co.)	1½ fluid ozs.	48.0 cc.

*To make 28% acetic acid from glacial acetic acid dilute 3 parts of glacial acetic acid with 8 parts of water.

[Formula SB-1a] **Acid Rinse Bath**
For Kodalith Films, Plates, and Paper and Kodalith Stripping Film (Normal)

	Avoirdupois	Metric
Water	1 gallon	1.0 liter
*Acetic Acid (28% pure) (E.K.Co.)	16 ounces	125.0 cc.

*To make 28% acetic acid from glacial acetic acid dilute 3 parts of glacial acetic acid with 8 parts of water.

The action of these baths instantly checks development and prevents uneven spots and streaks when the prints or negatives are immersed in the fixing bath.

[Formula SB-3] **Chrome Alum Hardening Bath**
For Films and Plates

In hot weather, the following hardening bath should be used after development and before fixation in conjunction with Formula F-5 or when F-16 does not harden sufficiently.

	Avoirdupois	Metric
Water	32 ounces	1.0 liter
Potassium Chrome Alum	1 ounce	30.0 grams

Agitate the negatives for about 30 seconds when first immersed in the hardener. Leave them in the bath for 3 minutes. This bath should be renewed frequently.

[Formula SB-4] **Tropical Hardening Bath**
For Films and Plates

	Avoirdupois	Metric
Water	32 ounces	1.0 liter
Potassium Chrome Alum	1 ounce	30.0 grams
*Sodium Sulfate, desiccated	2 ounces	60.0 grams

*If crystalline sodium sulfate is preferred instead of desiccated sulfate, use 4 ozs. 290 grains (140.0 grams) in the formula.

(*Continued on next page*)

FORMULAS

Agitate the negatives for 30 to 45 seconds when first immersing them in the hardener, or streakiness will result. Leave them in the bath for 3 minutes. The hardening bath is a violet-blue color by tungsten light when freshly mixed, but it ultimately turns a yellow-green with use; it then ceases to harden and should be replaced with a fresh bath. The hardening bath should never be over-worked. An unused bath will keep indefinitely, but the hardening properties of a partially used bath fall off rapidly on standing for a few days.

Nonswelling Acid Rinse Bath for Roll Film [Formula SB-5]

	Avoirdupois	Metric
Water	16 ounces	500.0 cc.
*Acetic Acid (28% pure) (E.K.Co.)	1 fluid oz.	32.0 cc.
**Sodium Sulfate, desiccated	1½ ounces	45.0 grams
Water to make	32 ounces	1.0 liter

*To make 28% acetic acid from glacial acetic acid, dilute 3 parts of glacial acetic acid with 8 parts of water.

**If it is desired to use sodium sulfate crystals instead of the desiccated sulfate, use 3½ ounces per quart (105 grams per liter).

Agitate the films when immersed in this bath and allow them to remain about 3 minutes before transfer to the fixing bath.

Formula SB-5 is satisfactory for use to 80° F. (26.5° C.). It should be replaced after processing about 100 rolls per gallon provided not more than 2½ quarts of developer (DK-60a) have been carried into the SB-5 bath by 100 rolls. *This rinse bath should not be revived with acid.*

When working at temperatures below 75° F. (24° C.), the life of the acid rinse bath may be extended by giving the films a few seconds' rinse in running water previous to immersion in the acid rinse bath.

FIXING BATHS

Acid Hardening Fixing Bath [Formula F-5]
For General Use with Films and Plates

	Avoirdupois	Metric
Water (about 125°) (F.52° C.)	20 ounces	600.0 cc.
Sodium Thiosulfate (Hypo)	8 ounces	240.0 grams
Sodium Sulfite, desiccated (E.K.Co.)	½ ounce	15.0 grams
*Acetic Acid (28% pure) (E.K.Co.)	1½ fluid ozs.	48.0 cc.
**Boric Acid, crystals	¼ ounce	7.5 grams
Potassium Alum (E.K.Co.)	½ ounce	15.0 grams
Cold water to make	32 ounces	1.0 liter

*To make 28% acetic acid from glacial acetic acid, dilute 3 parts of glacial acetic acid with 8 parts of water.

**Use crystalline boric acid as specified. Powdered boric acid dissolves with great difficulty.

(*Over*)

Dissolve the hypo in the specified volume of water (about 125° F. (52° C.) and then add the remaining chemicals in the order given, taking care that each chemical is dissolved before adding the next. Then dilute with water to the required volume.

Odorless Fixing Bath: The slight odor of sulfur dioxide given off by freshly mixed solutions of F-5 may be eliminated almost entirely by omitting the boric acid and substituting ½ ounce of Kodalk per quart of fixing bath (15 grams per liter). Provided an acid rinse bath (SB-1 or SB-3) is used previous to fixation, the capacity (life) of the odorless fixing bath will be about eighty to one hundred 8 x 10-inch films or plates (or their equivalent in other sizes) per gallon. With a water rinse, the capacity will be one-half as great as with an acid rinse. The modified bath will be known as Formula F-6.

The constituents of F-5 other than hypo may be compounded as a stock hardener solution to be added to a solution of hypo as follows:

[Formula F-5a] **Acid Hardener Stock Solution**

	Avoirdupois	Metric
Water (about 125° F.) (52° C.)	20 ounces	600.0 cc.
Sodium Sulfite, desiccated (E.K.Co.)	2½ ounces	75.0 grams
*Acetic Acid (28% pure) (E.K.Co.)	7½ fluid ozs.	235.0 cc.
**Boric Acid, crystals	1¼ ounces	37.5 grams
Potassium Alum (E.K.Co.)	2½ ounces	75.0 grams
Cold water to make	32 ounces	1.0 liter

*To make 28% acetic acid from glacial acetic acid, dilute 3 parts of glacial acetic acid with 8 parts of water.

**Use crystalline boric acid as specified. Powdered boric acid dissolves with great difficulty.

Dissolve chemicals in the order given.

Add one part of the cool stock hardener solution slowly to 4 parts of a cool 30% hypo solution, while stirring the hypo rapidly.

Odorless Stock Hardener: A stock hardener for mixing the odorless fixing bath (F-6) may be prepared by replacing the boric acid in F-5a with 2½ ounces of Kodalk per quart of hardener (75 grams per liter). One part of this hardener should be added slowly to 4 parts of cool 30% hypo solution, while stirring the hypo solution rapidly. This modified hardener will be known as F-6a.

Acid Hardening Fixing Bath [Formula F-10]
For Use with Highly Alkaline Developers

	Avoirdupois	Metric
Water (about 125° F.) (52° C.)	64 ounces	500.0 cc.
Sodium Thiosulfate (Hypo)	2¾ pounds	330.0 grams
Sodium Sulfite, desiccated (E.K.Co.)	1 ounce	7.5 grams
Kodalk	4 ounces	30.0 grams
*Acetic Acid (28% pure) (E.K.Co.)	9 fluid ozs.	70.0 cc.
Potassium Alum (E.K.Co.)	3 ounces	22.5 grams
Cold water to make	1 gallon	1.0 liter

*To make 28% acetic acid from glacial acid, dilute 3 parts of glacial acetic with 8 parts of water.

Dissolve the chemicals in the order given, taking care that each chemical is dissolved completely before adding the next.

The bath is especially recommended for use with D-19 or D-11 developers. Agitate the films or plates on first placing in the bath and at intervals until fixation is completed.

Fix for twice the time to clear the film of its milky appearance. Wash thoroughly and *wipe each negative carefully* before drying. When the time to clear has been increased, through use, to twice the time required with a fresh bath, the solution should be discarded.

Chrome Alum Fixing Bath [Formula F-16]
For Films and Plates

Solution A

	Avoirdupois	Metric
Sodium Thiosulfate (Hypo)	2 pounds	960.0 grams
Sodium Sulfite, desiccated (E.K.Co.)	2 ounces	60.0 grams
Water to make	96 ounces	3.0 liters

Solution B

	Avoirdupois	Metric
Water	32 ounces	1.0 liter
Potassium Chrome Alum	2 ounces	60.0 grams
Sulfuric Acid, C.P. (E.K.Co.)	¼ fluid oz.	8.0 cc.

Pour one part solution B into three parts solution A slowly while stirring A rapidly. This formula, when freshly mixed, is especially recommended for use in hot weather, but it rapidly loses its hardening properties with or without use, when it should be replaced by a fresh bath.

[Formula F-23] **Chrome Alum Fixing Bath**
For Motion Picture Films
For Use at 75° to 90° F. (24° to 32° C.)

Solution A

	Avoirdupois	Metric
*Sodium Thiosulfate (Hypo)	240 pounds	240.0 grams
Sodium Sulfite, desiccated (E.K.Co.)	12½ pounds	12.5 grams
Water to make	90 gallons	750.0 cc.

*A bath which fixes more rapidly may be obtained by increasing the hypo concentration in the above formula to 2½ lbs. per gallon (1200 grams per 4 liters).

Solution B

	Avoirdupois	Metric
Water	20 gallons	150.0 cc.
Sodium Sulfite, desiccated (E.K.Co.)	5 pounds	5.0 grams
*Sulfuric Acid 5%	4¾ gallons	40.0 cc.
Potassium Chrome Alum	32 pounds	32.0 grams
Water to make	30 gallons	250.0 cc.

*To prepare 5% sulfuric acid, add one part by volume of sulfuric acid, C.P. (E.K.Co.) to 19 parts by volume of cold water, and mix carefully with stirring. The acid must be added to the water, otherwise the solution may boil with explosive violence and if spattered on the hands or face, will cause serious burns.

Directions: Dissolve the constituents of solution A and *cool to 70° F. (21° C.).* Mix solution B by adding the chemicals in the order given and *cool to 70° F. (21° C.).* Then add solution B slowly to solution A while stirring the latter solution thoroughly. If solutions A and B are not cool when mixed, the bath will sulfurize.

If the solutions are mixed in a deep tank and the hypo bath is not stirred adequately, the chrome alum solution will tend to float on top of the hypo solution and sulfurization is apt to occur. Solution B should not be stored as a stock solution because it will lose its hardening properties.

[Formula F-25] **Acid Hardening Fixing Bath**
For Motion Picture Films

	Avoirdupois	Metric
Sodium Thiosulfate (Hypo)	300 pounds	300.0 grams
*Sodium Sulfite, desiccated (E.K.Co.)	5 pounds	5.0 grams
Acetic Acid, glacial	1 gallon 26 fluid ozs.	10.0 cc.
**Boric Acid, crystals	5 pounds	5.0 grams
Potassium Alum (E.K.Co.)	10 pounds	10.0 grams
Water to make	120 gallons	1.0 liter

*This bath contains a minimum quantity of sulfite, which is such that the bath will not sulfurize within a period of 3 to 4 weeks at 70° F. (21° C.). If the temperature is likely to rise above 70° F. (21° C.), twice the quantity of sulfite should be used.

**Crystalline boric acid should be used as specified. Powdered boric acid dissolves only with great difficulty, and its use should be avoided.

Dissolve the hypo in one-half the required volume of water and then add the remaining chemicals in the order given after dissolving in a small quantity of water. Dilute with water to the required volume.

FORMULAS

Non-Hardening Fixing Bath [Formula F-24]

	Avoirdupois	Metric
Water (about 125° F.) (52° C.) . . .	16 ounces	500.0 cc.
Sodium Thiosulfate (Hypo)	8 ounces	240.0 grams
Sodium Sulfite, desiccated (E.K.Co.) .	145 grains	10.0 grams
Sodium Bisulfite (E.K.Co.)	365 grains	25.0 grams
Cold water to make	32 ounces	1.0 liter

Dissolve chemicals in the order given.

This bath is recommended for films, plates or paper when no hardening is desired.

Acid Hardening Fixing Bath for Papers [Formula F-1]

	Avoirdupois	Metric
Water	64 ounces	1.0 liter
Sodium Thiosulfate (Hypo)	16 ounces	240.0 grams

Then add the following hardener solution slowly to the cool hypo solution while stirring the latter rapidly.

Water (about 125° F.) (52° C.) . . .	5 ounces	80.0 cc.
Sodium Sulfite, desiccated (E.K.Co.) .	1 ounce	15.0 grams
*Acetic Acid (28% pure) (E.K.Co.) . .	3 fluid ozs.	48.0 cc.
Potassium Alum (E.K.Co.)	1 ounce	15.0 grams

*To make 28% acetic acid from glacial acetic acid, dilute 3 parts of glacial acetic acid with 8 parts of water.

Dissolve chemicals in the order given.

If it is desired to mix a stock hardener solution, use F-1a:

Acid Hardener Stock Solution [Formula F-1a]

	Avoirdupois	Metric
Water (about 125° F.) (52° C.) . . .	56 ounces	425.0 cc.
Sodium Sulfite, desiccated (E.K.Co.) .	8 ounces	60.0 grams
*Acetic Acid (28% pure) (E.K.Co.) . .	24 fluid ozs.	188.0 cc.
Potassium Alum (E.K.Co.)	8 ounces	60.0 grams
Cold water to make	1 gallon	1.0 liter

*To make 28% acetic acid from glacial acetic acid, dilute 3 parts of glacial acetic acid with 8 parts of water.

To make up the hardener dissolve chemicals in the order given. The sodium sulfite should be dissolved completely before adding the acetic acid. After the sulfite-acid solution has been mixed thoroughly, add the potassium alum with constant stirring. If the hypo is not thoroughly dissolved before adding hardener a sulfur precipitate may be formed.

For use, add one part of cool stock hardener solution slowly to 4 parts of a cool 25% hypo solution while stirring the hypo rapidly.

Washing Test and Hypo Elimination

Very small traces of hypo retained in films or prints greatly accelerate the rate of fading of the image. It is extremely difficult to test for small quantities of hypo but the following test (Formula HT-1a) will indicate when the film or prints may be considered reasonably free from hypo.

When complete removal of hypo is important, prints should be treated in the HE-1 Hypo Eliminator. (See page 121).

[Formula HT-1a]   **Hypo Test Solution**

	Avoirdupois	Metric
Distilled Water	6 ounces	180.0 cc.
Potassium Permanganate	4 grains	0.3 gram
Sodium Hydroxide (Caustic Soda)	8 grains	0.6 gram
Water (distilled) to make	8 ounces	250.0 cc.

To make the test with film take 8 ounces (250 cc.) of pure water in a clear glass and add ¼ dram (one cc.) of the permanganate-caustic soda solution.

Then take a 6- or 8-exposure film, No. 118 or No. 616 or equivalent from the wash water and allow the water from it to drip for 30 seconds into the glass of test solution. If a small percentage of hypo is present the violet color will turn orange in *about 30 seconds* and with a larger concentration the orange color will change to yellow. In either case the film should be returned to the wash water and allowed to remain until further tests produce no change in the violet color which proves that the hypo content has been reduced to a safe margin, thereby insuring satisfactory permanency.

To make the test with prints take 4 ounces (125 cc.) of pure water in a clear glass and add ¼ dram (one cc.) of the permanganate-caustic soda solution. Pour ½ ounce (15 cc.) of this diluted solution into a clear one ounce glass container.

Then take six prints, size 4 x 5-inch or equivalent, from the wash water and allow the water from them to drip for 30 seconds into the ½ ounce of the dilute test solution. If a small quantity of hypo is present the violet color will turn orange in *about 30 seconds* and become colorless in one minute. In either case the prints should be returned to the wash water and allowed to remain until further tests show that the hypo content has been reduced to a safe margin, thereby insuring satisfactory permanency.

Note: Oxidizable organic matter if present in the water reacts with the permanganate solution and changes its color in the same manner as hypo.

Hypo Eliminator　　　[Formula HE-1]

	Avoirdupois	Metric
Water	16 ounces	500.0 cc.
Hydrogen Peroxide (3% solution)*	4 fluid ozs.	125.0 cc.
Ammonia (3% solution)**	3¼ fluid ozs.	100.0 cc.
Water to make	32 ounces	1.0 liter

*Commercial hydrogen peroxide (pharmaceutical grade) is approximately a 3 per cent solution.

**Kodak Ammonia is supplied as a 3 per cent solution or Concentrated Ammonia (28 %) may be diluted by taking 1 part 28 per cent ammonia to 9 parts of water.

Directions for Use: Wash the prints for about 30 minutes at 65° to 70° F. in running water which flows rapidly enough to replace the water in the vessel (tray or tank) completely once every 5 minutes. Then immerse each print about 6 minutes at 70° F. in the HE-1 Hypo Eliminator solution and finally wash about 10 minutes before drying. At lower temperatures, increase the washing times.

Life of HE-1 Solution: About fifty 8 x 10-inch prints or their equivalent per gallon (4 liters).

Test for Hypo: Process with the batch of prints, an unexposed *white* sheet of photographic paper (same weight and size as majority of prints in batch). After a final wash, cut off a strip of this sheet and immerse it in a 1 per cent silver nitrate solution for about 3 minutes; then rinse in water and compare *while wet* with the *wet untreated portion*. If the hypo has been completely removed, no color difference should be observed. A yellow-brown tint indicates the presence of hypo. The depth of the tint increases with increased hypo content. A positive test with silver nitrate may also be obtained in the absence of hypo if hydrogen sulfide or wood extracts are present in the water supply.

REDUCTION, and INTENSIFICATION

If negatives need aftertreatment, it is best to treat them immediately after they have been hardened and washed.

Precautions: Stains are sometimes produced during reduction, intensification, and stain removal unless the following precautions are observed: (1) The negative should be hardened in the Formalin Hardener (SH-1) before the intensification or reduction treatment. (2) The negative should be fixed and washed thoroughly before treatment and be free of scum or stain. (3) Only one negative should be handled at a time and it should be agitated thoroughly during the treatment; then washed thoroughly and wiped off carefully before drying.

[Formula SH-1] Formalin Hardener
For Films and Plates

	Avoirdupois	Metric
Water	16 ounces	500.0 cc.
Formalin (40% Formaldehyde solution)	2½ drams	10.0 cc.
Sodium Carbonate, desiccated (E.K.Co.)	73 grains	5.0 grams
Water to make	32 ounces	1.0 liter

This formula is recommended for the treatment of negatives which would normally be softened considerably by a chemical treatment in the removal of several types of stains, or by intensification or reduction.

After hardening in SH-1 for three minutes, negatives should always be rinsed and immersed in either a 2% acetic acid solution or a fresh acid fixing bath and well washed before further treatment, otherwise stains will be produced, particularly with the Mercury Intensifier (Formula In-1).

REDUCERS

Eastman reducer formulas may be classified according to their use as follows:

1. Cutting or Subtractive Reducers for Correcting Overexposed Negatives.
    R-2 Acid Permanganate
    R-4a Farmer's (single solution) Reducer
2. Proportional Reducers for Correcting Overdeveloped Negatives.
    R-4b Two-Solution Farmer's Reducer
    R-5 Acid Permanganate-Persulfate
    R-7 Ferric Alum (for motion picture work)
    R-8 Modified Belitski (Also a cutting reducer).
3. Super-Proportional Reducer for Correcting Overdeveloped Negatives of Contrasty Subjects.
    R-1 Acid-Persulfate.

[Formula R-2] Permanganate Reducer
For Correcting Overexposed Negatives

Stock Solution A

	Avoirdupois	Metric
Water	32 ounces	1.0 liter
Potassium Permanganate	1¾ ounces	52.5 grams

(Continued on next page)

Stock Solution B

	Avoirdupois	Metric
Cold water	32 ounces	1.0 liter
Sulfuric Acid, C.P. (E.K.Co.)	1 fluid oz.	32.0 cc.

The best method of dissolving the permanganate crystals in Solution A is to use a small volume of hot water (about 180° F.) (82° C.) and shake or stir the solution vigorously until completely dissolved; then dilute to volume with cold water. When preparing Stock Solution B, *always add the sulfuric acid to the water slowly with stirring and never the water to the acid*, otherwise the solution may boil and spatter the acid on the hands or face causing serious burns.

NOTE: If a scum forms on the top of the permanganate solution or a reddish curd appears in the solution, it is because the negative has not been sufficiently washed to remove all hypo, or because the permanganate solution has been contaminated by hypo. The separate solutions will keep and work perfectly for a considerable time if proper precautions against contamination are observed. The two solutions should not be combined until immediately before use. They will not keep long in combination.

A close observance of the foregoing instructions is important. Otherwise an iridescent scum will sometimes appear on the reduced negatives after they are dry; and this is difficult, if not impossible, to remove.

This solution should not be used as a stain remover as it tends to attack the image before it removes the stain. Use Formula S-6, page 142, for removal of stain.

Harden the negative first in the special hardener (Formula SH-1, page 122. The negative must be washed thoroughly to remove all the traces of hypo before it is reduced.

For use, take stock solution A, one dram (4 cc.), stock solution B, 2 drams (8 cc.), water 8 ounces (250 cc.). When the negative has been reduced sufficiently, immerse in a fresh acid fixing bath for a few minutes, to remove yellow stain, and then wash thoroughly. If reduction is too rapid, use more water when diluting.

Farmer's Reducer [Formula R-4]
For Amateur Use
For Correcting Overexposed Negatives

Solution A

	Avoirdupois	Metric
Water	1 ounce	32.0 cc.
Potassium Ferricyanide	15 grains	1.0 gram

Solution B

	Avoirdupois	Metric
Water	32 ounces	1.0 liter
Sodium Thiosulfate (Hypo)	1 ounce	30.0 grams

Add A to B and immediately pour over the negative to be reduced which has first been treated with the special formalin hardener solution (SH-1, page 122). The formula should be prepared immediately before using as it decomposes rapidly after mixing together the A and B solutions. When the negative has been reduced sufficiently, wash thoroughly before drying. Local areas may be reduced with this reducer by applying the solution with a cotton pad.

ELEMENTARY PHOTOGRAPHIC CHEMISTRY

[Formula R-4a]   **Farmer's Reducer**
For all Professional Films and Plates
For Correcting Overexposed Negatives

*Stock Solution A

	Avoirdupois	Metric
Potassium Ferricyanide	1¼ ounces	37.5 grams
Water to make	16 ounces	500.0 cc.

Stock Solution B

	Avoirdupois	Metric
Sodium Thiosulfate (Hypo)	16 ounces	480.0 grams
Water to make	64 ounces	2.0 liter

*Store in a brown bottle and shield from strong daylight.

For use take: Stock Solution A, one ounce (30 cc.), stock solution B, 4 ounces (120 cc.), and water to make 32 ounces (one liter). Add A to B, then add the water.

Harden the negative first with the special hardener (SH-1, page 122).

Pour the mixed solution at once over the negative to be reduced. Watch closely. The action is best seen when the solution is poured over the negative in a white tray. When the negative has been reduced sufficiently, wash thoroughly before drying.

Solutions A and B should not be combined until they are to be used. They will not keep long in combination.

[Formula R-4b]   **Two-Solution Farmer's Reducer**
For Correcting Overdeveloped Negatives

Farmer's Reducer also may be used as a two-solution formula by treating the negative in the ferricyanide solution first and subsequently in the hypo solution. This method has the advantage of giving almost proportional reduction and correcting for over-development. The single solution Farmer's Reducer gives only cutting reduction and corrects for overexposure.

*Solution A

	Avoirdupois	Metric
Potassium Ferricyanide	¼ ounce	7.5 grams
Water to make	32 ounces	1.0 liter

Solution B

	Avoirdupois	Metric
Sodium Thiosulfate (Hypo)	6¾ ounces	200.0 grams
Water to make	32 ounces	1.0 liter

*Store in a brown bottle and shield from strong daylight.

After hardening in the special hardener (SH-1, page 122) and washing thoroughly, treat the negatives in Solution A with uniform agitation for one to 4 minutes at 65° to 70° F.

(Continued on next page)

(18° to 21° C.) depending on the degree of reduction desired. Then immerse them in Solution B for 5 minutes and wash thoroughly. The process may be repeated if more reduction is desired. For the reduction of general fog, one part of Solution A should be diluted with one part of water.

Proportional Reducer [Formula R-5]
For Correcting Overdeveloped Negatives

Stock Solution A

	Avoirdupois	Metric
Water	32 ounces	1.0 liter
Potassium Permanganate	4 grains	0.3 gram
*Sulfuric Acid (10% solution)	½ fluid oz.	16.0 cc.

Stock Solution B

	Avoirdupois	Metric
Water	96 ounces	3.0 liters
Ammonium Persulfate	3 ounces	90.0 grams

*To make a 10% solution of sulfuric acid take one part of concentrated acid and add it to 9 parts of water, slowly with stirring.

For use, take one part of A to 3 parts of B. Treat the negative first in the special hardener (SH-1, page 122) and wash thoroughly. When sufficient reduction is secured the negative should be immersed in a fresh acid fixing bath, such as F-5, page 115. Wash the negative thoroughly before drying.

Ferric Alum Proportional Reducer [Formula R-7]
For Correcting Overdeveloped Motion Picture Negatives

	Avoirdupois	Metric
Water	1 gallon	1.0 liter
Sulfuric Acid, C.P. (E.K.Co.)	1¼ fluid ozs.	10.0 cc.
Ferric Ammonium Sulfate (ferric alum)	2 ounces	15.0 grams

When mixing the formula, be careful to add the acid to the water solution and not the water to the acid, or the solution will boil with explosive violence.

Use the reducer full strength at 65° to 70° F. (18° to 21° C.). Films should be hardened with the alkaline hardener solution (Formula SH-1, page 122) and washed before treatment with the reducer solution. *Important: Avoid contact with the air during reduction and washing as stains will result. Avoid contamination of this solution with hypo which shortens its life.* Wash thoroughly after treating with the reducer.

126 ELEMENTARY PHOTOGRAPHIC CHEMISTRY

[Formula R-8] **Modified Belitski Reducer**
For Correcting Overexposed and Overdeveloped Negatives

	Avoirdupois	Metric
Water (about 125° F.) (52° C.)	24 ounces	750.0 cc.
Ferric Chloride	365 grains	25.0 grams
*Potassium Citrate	2½ ounces	75.0 grams
Sodium Sulfite, desiccated (E.K.Co.)	1 ounce	30.0 grams
Citric Acid	290 grains	20.0 grams
Sodium Thiosulfate (Hypo)	6¾ ounces	200.0 grams
Water to make	32 ounces	1.0 liter

*Sodium citrate should not be used because it slows up the rate of reduction.

Dissolve chemicals in the order given.

Use full strength for maximum rate of reduction. Treat negatives first in the special hardener (SH-1, page 122) and wash thoroughly. Then immerse in R-8 for one to 10 minutes at 65° to 70° F. (18° to 21° C.). Wash thoroughly. If a slower action is desired, dilute one part of solution with one part of water. The reducer is specially suitable for treatment of dense, contrasty negatives.

[Formula R-1] **Persulfate Reducer**
For Overdeveloped Negatives of [a] Contrasty Subjects
Stock Solution

	Avoirdupois	Metric
Water	32 ounces	1.0 liter
Ammonium Persulfate	2 ounces	60.0 grams
Sulfuric Acid, C.P. (E.K.Co.)	¾ dram	3.0 cc.

For use, take one part stock solution and 2 parts water.

Treat the negative in the special hardener (SH-1, page 122) and wash thoroughly.

When reduction is complete, immerse in an acid fixing bath for a few minutes, then wash. If reduction is too rapid, dilute the solution with a further volume of water.

[Formula In-1] **INTENSIFIERS**
Mercury Intensifier

The mercury intensifier is recommended where extreme intensification is desired and where permanence of the resulting image is not essential. If permanence is essential either the chromium or the silver intensifiers should be used.

(Continued on next page)

After hardening in the special hardener (SH-1, page 122) and washing thoroughly, bleach the negative in the following solution until the image turns white; then wash for at least 10 to 15 minutes:

	Avoirdupois	Metric
Potassium Bromide	¾ ounce	22.5 grams
*Mercuric Chloride	¾ ounce	22.5 grams
Water to make	32 ounces	1.0 liter

*The chemical is highly poisonous and should be handled with the same care as any known virulent poison.

The negative should then be blackened with 10% sulfite solution; or with a developing solution, such as Formula D-72 (diluted 1 to 2); or with 10% ammonia (one part concentrated ammonia [28%] to 9 parts water), these giving progressively greater contrast in the order given. To increase contrast greatly, treat with the following solution:

Solution A

	Avoirdupois	Metric
Water	16 ounces	500.0 cc.
*Sodium Cyanide	½ ounce	15.0 grams

Solution B

	Avoirdupois	Metric
Water	16 ounces	500.0 cc.
Silver Nitrate, crystals	¾ ounce	22.5 grams

To prepare the intensifier, add the silver nitrate Solution B to the cyanide Solution A until a permanent precipitate is just produced; allow the mixture to stand a short time and filter. *This is called Monckhoven's Intensifier.*

Redevelopment cannot be controlled as by the chromium method (Formula In-4) but must go to completion.

Warning: Cyanide is a deadly poison and should be handled with extreme care. Use rubber gloves and avoid exposure to fumes. Cyanide reacts with acid to form poisonous hydrogen cyanide gas. When discarding a solution containing cyanide, always run water to flush it out of the sink quickly. Cyanide solutions should never be used in poorly ventilated rooms.

Note: See precautions on handling negatives, pages 121 and 122.

Chromium Intensifier [Formula In-4]
Stock Solution

	Avoirdupois	Metric
Potassium Bichromate	3 ounces	90.0 grams
Hydrochloric Acid, C.P. (E.K.Co.)	2 fluid ozs.	64.0 cc.
Water to make	32 ounces	1.0 liter

Harden the negative first in the special hardener (SH-1, page 122) and wash. For use, take one part of stock solution to 10 parts of water. Bleach thoroughly at 65° to 70° F. (18° to 21° C.), then wash 5 minutes and re-develop fully (about 5 minutes) in artificial light or daylight (not direct sunlight) in any quick-acting, non-staining developer con-

(Over)

taining the normal proportion of bromide such as Nepera Solution diluted 1:4 or in the Elon-Hydroquinone developer (Formula D-72) diluted 1:3. Then wash thoroughly and dry. Greater intensification can be secured by repeating the process. The degree of intensification can be controlled by varying the time of re-development.

Warning: Developers containing a high concentration of sulfite such as D-76 are not suitable for re-development since the sulfite tends to dissolve the silver chloride before the developing agents have time to act on it.

The Eastman Chromium Intensifier Powders are equally as satisfactory as Formula In-4, and are supplied in prepared form ready to use simply by dissolving in water.

Note: See precautions on handling negatives, pages 121 and 122.

[Formula]   **Silver Intensifier**
[In-5]   For General Use on Films or Plates

The following formula is the only intensifier known that will not change the color of the image on positive film on projection. It gives proportional intensification and is easily controlled by varying the time of treatment. The formula is equally suitable for positive and negative film. *Caution:* The intensifier solution should be mixed and used only in artificial (not arc) light since its stability and degree of intensification are affected by daylight.

Negatives should preferably be hardened in the special formalin hardener (SH-1, page 122) before treating in the intensifier solution.

Stock Solution No. 1
(Store in a brown bottle)

	Avoirdupois	Metric
Silver Nitrate, crystals (E.K.Co.)	2 ounces	60.0 grams
Distilled water to make	32 ounces	1.0 liter

Stock Solution No. 2

	Avoirdupois	Metric
Sodium Sulfite, desiccated (E.K.Co.)	2 ounces	60.0 grams
Water to make	32 ounces	1.0 liter

Stock Solution No. 3

	Avoirdupois	Metric
Sodium Thiosulfate (Hypo)	3½ ounces	105.0 grams
Water to make	32 ounces	1.0 liter

Stock Solution No. 4

	Avoirdupois	Metric
Sodium Sulfite, desiccated (E.K.Co.)	½ ounce	15.0 grams
Elon	350 grains	24.0 grams
Water to make	96 ounces	3.0 liters

(Continued on next page)

FORMULAS

Prepare the intensifier solution for use as follows: Slowly add one part of solution No. 1 to one part of solution No. 2, shaking or stirring to obtain thorough mixing. The white precipitate which appears is then dissolved by the addition of one part of solution No. 3. Allow the resulting solution to stand a few minutes until clear. Then add, with stirring, 3 parts of solution No. 4. The intensifier is then ready for use and the film should be treated immediately. The mixed intensifier solution is stable for approximately 30 minutes at 70° F. (21° C.).

The degree of intensification obtained depends upon the time of treatment which should not exceed 25 minutes. After intensification, immerse the film for 2 minutes with agitation in a plain 30% hypo solution. Then wash thoroughly.

The stability of the mixed intensifier solution and the rate of intensification are very sensitive to changes in the thiosulfate concentration. A more active but less stable working solution may be obtained by using a stock solution No. 3 prepared with 3 ounces of hypo per 32 ounces (90 grams per liter) instead of the quantity in the formula. The directions for preparing the working solution are the same as before but the mixed intensifier will not keep over 20 minutes at 70° F. (21° C.).

For best results, the intensifier should be used in artificial light; the solution tends to form a precipitate of silver quite rapidly when exposed directly to sunlight.

Note: See precautions on handling negatives, pages 121 and 122.

Re-Development Intensifier

Perhaps the simplest method of intensificaton for negatives consists of bleaching in the ferricyanide and bromide formula used for the sepia toning of prints (Formula T-7a, page 138) and blackening with sodium sulfide exactly as in print toning.

TONING FORMULAS

A. Toning Baths for Lantern Slides, Transparencies, and Motion Picture Prints.

Three distinct methods of toning are possible:
(1) Toning by direct development.
(2) Toning by replacement of the silver image with inorganic salts (metal tones).
(3) Toning with dyes (dye tones).

(*Over*)

1. Toning by Direct Development

The color of the silver image produced by development is determined by the size of the silver particles composing the image, and it is possible to control the size of these particles and therefore the color of the image by modifying the nature of the developer.

The developer (Formula D-32) on page 110 will give pleasing warm black tones.

The range of colors obtainable, however, is not very great and it is usually easier and more certain to produce such slight modifications of color either by delicate dye tinting or by giving a short immersion in one of the diluted toning baths.

2. Toning by Replacement of the Silver Image with Inorganic Salts

Since most toning processes intensify the original silver image, it is best to commence with a slide or positive print which is somewhat on the thin side. Experience will dictate the most suitable image quality with various toning processes which yields the best results.

Stability of Solutions. All toning baths containing potassium ferricyanide are sensitive to light, the ferricyanide being reduced to ferrocyanide, with the resulting formation of a sludge of the metallic ferrocyanide. When not in use, tanks should be covered to prevent exposure to daylight and small volumes of solution should be placed in dark brown bottles.

It is also very important that no metallic surface, however small, should come in contact with the solutions. Wooden or stoneware tanks with hard rubber faucets should be used. Motion picture film should be wound on wooden racks, free of metal pegs.

[Formula T-9] **Uranium Toner**
For Brown to Red Tones on Slides or Films

	Avoirdupois		Metric
Uranium (Uranyl) Nitrate	2½ pounds	35 grains	2.5 grams
Potassium Oxalate	2½ pounds	35 grains	2.5 grams
Potassium Ferricyanide	1 pound	15 grains	1.0 gram
Ammonium Alum	6 pounds	85 grains	6.0 grams
Hydrochloric Acid, 10% solution	77 fluid ozs.	1¼ drams	5.0 cc.
Water to make	120 gallons	32 ounces	1.0 liter

Dissolve chemicals in the order given.

The solution should be perfectly clear and pale yellow in color. *It is light sensitive, however, and should be stored in the dark.* The maximum degree of toning is produced in about 10 minutes, the tone passing from brown to red during this time.

It is convenient to keep 10% stock solutions of the constituent chemicals of the above toning bath for quick compounding of a new bath.

For motion picture work, 120 gallons of the above bath will tone about 12,000 feet of film without any appreciable change in the tone. A volume of acid may then be added equal to that originally used, when a further 12,000 feet may be toned. After toning the second quantity of film, the bath should be discarded.

After toning, wash for about 10 minutes, though the washing should not be prolonged especially if the water is slightly alkaline since the toned image is soluble in alkali.

Sulfide Toner [Formula T-10]
For Sepia Tones on Lantern Slides

Solution A

	Avoirdupois	Metric
Potassium Ferricyanide	1 ounce	30.0 grams
Potassium Bromide	½ ounce	15.0 grams
Water to make	32 ounces	1.0 liter

Solution B

	Avoirdupois	Metric
*Sodium Sulfide, fused (not sulfite)	13 grains	0.9 gram
Water to make	32 ounces	1.0 liter

*Use three times the quantity of crystalline sodium sulfide.

The well washed slide is thoroughly bleached in A, washed for 5 minutes, and immersed in Solution B for about 2 minutes until thoroughly toned. The slide should then be washed thoroughly for 10 to 15 minutes before drying. The transparency of the tone is much improved by the addition of a little hypo to the B solution, say, 64 grains per 32 ounces or 4.5 grams per liter.

Sulfide Toner [Formula T-10a]
For Sepia Tones on Motion Picture Film

Solution A

	Avoirdupois	Metric
Potassium Ferricyanide	20 pounds	20.0 grams
Potassium Bromide	5 pounds	5.0 grams
Water to make	120 gallons	1.0 liter

(Over)

Solution B

	Avoirdupois	Metric
*Sodium Sulfide, fused (not sulfite) . .	1 lb. 10½ ozs.	1.7 grams
Water to make	120 gallons	1.0 liter

*Use 3 times the quantity of crystalline sodium sulfide.

The well washed positive should be bleached thoroughly in 2 to 4 minutes in A at 65° to 70° F. (18° to 21° C.), so that the image appears uniformly yellow on looking at the back of the film. Then wash 5 minutes and immerse in solution B until the film is thoroughly toned. A trace of iron in the sodium sulfide will do no harm provided the solution is boiled and the precipitated iron sulfide allowed to settle before use. Wash 10 to 15 minutes after sulfiding and before drying.

[Formula T-11]   **Iron Toner**
For Blue Tones on Slides or Films

	Avoirdupois		Metric
Ammonium Persulfate . .	½ pound	7 grains	0.5 gram
Iron and Ammonium Sulfate (Ferric Alum) . .	1 lb. 6½ ozs.	20 grains	1.4 grams
Oxalic Acid	3 pounds	45 grains	3.0 grams
Potassium Ferricyanide . .	1 pound	15 grains	1.0 gram
Ammonium Alum . . .	5 pounds	75 grains	5.0 grams
Hydrochloric Acid, 10% .	15¼ fluid ozs.	¼ dram	1.0 cc.
Water to make	120 gallons	32 ounces	1.0 liter

Dissolve chemicals in the order given.

The method of compounding this bath is very important. Each of the solid chemicals should be dissolved separately in a small volume of water, the solutions then mixed strictly in the order given, and the whole diluted to the required volume. If these instructions are followed, the bath will be pale yellow in color and perfectly clear.

Immerse the slides or films from 2 to 10 minutes at 70° F. (21° C.) until the desired tone is obtained. Wash for 10 to 15 minutes until the highlights are clear. A very slight permanent yellow coloration of the clear gelatin will usually occur, but should be too slight to be detectable on projection. If the highlights are stained blue, then either the slide (film) was fogged during development, or the toning bath was stale or not mixed correctly.

Since the toned image is soluble in alkali, washing should not be carried out for too long a period, especially if the water is slightly alkaline.

Life of the Bath for Motion Picture Work. If the acid is renewed after toning each 5,000 feet, the bath is capable of toning 36,000 feet per 120 gallons of solution.

Mixed Iron and Uranium Tones

By mixing the uranium (T-9, page 130) and iron (T-11, page 132) toning solutions in different proportions, tones ranging from reddish-brown to chocolate are produced.

Analogous results may be obtained by immersing in each solution successively for varying times.

3. Dye Toning

It is not possible to obtain more than a limited number of tones by the use of colored inorganic compounds owing to the limited number of such compounds. Certain inorganic compounds, however, such as silver ferrocyanide can be used as mordants for basic dyes such as Victoria Green, Safranine, etc. If, therefore, a silver image is converted more or less to a silver ferrocyanide image and then immersed in a solution of a basic dye, a mordanted dye image is produced.

An uranium mordanting bath of the following composition is recommended for either films or slides:

Uranium Mordanting Bath [Formula T-17]

Stock Solution

	Avoirdupois		Metric
Uranium (Uranyl) Nitrate	8 pounds	116 grains	8.0 grams
Oxalic Acid	4 pounds	58 grains	4.0 grams
Potassium Ferricyanide	4 pounds	58 grains	4.0 grams
Water to make	120 gallons	32 ounces	1.0 liter

Directions for Mixing: The uranyl nitrate should be of good quality and should not contain an excess of free nitric acid. First dissolve each chemical separately in a small volume of water. Then add the oxalic acid solution to the uranyl nitrate solution and finally add the ferricyanide solution. If the uranyl nitrate is added directly to the potassium ferricyanide, a brown precipitate will be obtained which will not dissolve readily in the oxalic acid. After mixing, the bath should be light yellow and perfectly clear. The solution should not be exposed to light any more than necessary.

For use, take one part of stock solution and 4 parts water.

Time of Mordanting: Immerse the film (slide) at 65° to 70° F. (18° to 21° C.) until a very slight chocolate colored tone is obtained and remove at once. If mordanting is prolonged, much beyond this point, inferior tones will be produced. With a new bath this will require from 1½ to 2

(*Over*)

minutes but the time will need to be increased as the bath ages. The solution may be revived at intervals by adding a little of the concentrated stock solution.

Life of Bath. For motion picture work, the bath should be discarded after mordanting 22,000 feet of film per 120 gallons of solution.

Time of Washing after Mordanting. Wash until the highlights are free from yellow stain which usually takes about 10 to 15 minutes. Do not prolong the washing for more than 20 minutes or some of the mordant will be washed out.

An alternative mordanting bath is the following formula suggested by L. Chalkley, Jr.* The solution has the advantage that the mordanted image is practically colorless and highly transparent.

	Avoirdupois	Metric
Copper Sulfate	1 oz. 145 grains	40.0 grams
**Potassium Citrate, crystal	8 ozs. 165 grains	250.0 grams
Acetic Acid, glacial	1 fluid oz.	30.0 cc.
Ammonium Thiocyanate	365 grains	25.0 grams
(or Potassium Thiocyanate)	(424 grains)	(29.0 grams)
Water to make	32 ounces	1.0 liter

*"Two-Color Transparencies" by Lyman Chalkley, Jr., 1929 Amer. Annual of Photography, Amer. Phot. Publishing Co., Boston, Mass. pp. 23-31.

**Sodium citrate, crystal, may be substituted in equal weights for potassium citrate.

Dissolve the copper sulfate, potassium citrate, and acetic acid in about 800 cc. (26 ounces) of water. Dissolve the thiocyanate separately in 50 cc. (1¾ ounces) of water and add to the other solution. Dilute to volume.

This bath will keep for months without deterioration and may be used over again several times. With continued use a white flocculent precipitate may appear, but this does no harm. When it begins to work too slowly, it should be discarded.

⎡Formula⎤
⎣ T-17a ⎦   **The Dye Bath**

	Avoirdupois		Metric
Dye	3¼ ounces	3 grains	0.2 gram
*Acetic Acid, 10%	....	1¼ drams	5.0 cc. or
Acetic Acid, glacial	7¾ fluid ozs.	....	1.4 cc.
Water to make	120 gallons	32 ounces	1.0 liter

*To convert glacial acetic acid into 10% acetic, take one part glacial acetic acid and add it slowly to 9 parts of water.

Thoroughly dissolve the dye in hot water, filter, add the acid and dilute to volume with cold water.

The following dyes are suitable for toning:

Safranine A	Red	Victoria Green	Green
Chrysoidine 3R	Orange	Methylene Blue BB	Blue
Auramine	Yellow	*Methyl Violet	Violet

*For methyl violet use one-quarter the quantity of dye given in the formula.

Note: The dyes listed are obtainable from the Eastman Kodak Company, Rochester, N. Y., in quantities under one pound.

Time of Dye Toning. Immerse the mordanted and washed film (slide) in the dye bath for 2 to 15 minutes at 70° F. (21° C.) according to the color desired. The quantity of dye which mordants to the image increases with time. In case an image is over-dyed, some of the dye may be removed by immersing in a 0.2% solution of ammonia; then rinse before drying.

If, after dyeing 10 minutes, the image does not mordant sufficient dye, remove the film (slide), wash thoroughly, immerse again in the mordanting bath, wash, and re-dye.

Intermediate Dye Tones. Intermediate colors may be obtained either by mixing the dye solutions of T-17a or by immersing the film (slide) in successive baths. For example, if a reddish-orange tone is desired, first tone for a short time in the Safranine bath and then in the Chrysoidine bath, or the two baths may be mixed in suitable proportions and the tone secured with a single treatment.

Double Tones. It has been found that by omitting the ammonium alum from the iron toning formula, the half-tones of the toned slide are white and the shadows blue. If this image is then immersed in any of the basic dye solutions as used for dye toning (Formula T-17a), the dye is mordanted to the half-tones while the shadows remain more or less blue. By varying the dye solution used, the color of the half-tones may be varied at will.

Double Toning Bath [Formula T-18]

	Avoirdupois		Metric
Ammonium Persulfate .	½ pound	7 grains	0.5 gram
Iron and Ammonium Sulfate (Ferric Alum) .	1 lb. 6½ ozs.	20 grains	1.4 grams
Oxalic Acid	3 pounds	45 grains	3.2 grams
Potassium Ferricyanide .	1 pound	15 grains	1.0 gram
Hydrochloric Acid, 10% .	15¼ fluid ozs.	¼ dram	1.0 cc.
Water to make . . .	120 gallons	32 ounces	1.0 liter

The instructions for preparing the bath are the same as for the Iron toning bath (Formula T-11, page 132).

Directions for Use: Tone until the shadows are deep blue. Then wash 10 to 15 minutes. Immerse in the basic dye solution used for dye toning for 5 to 15 minutes until the desired depth of color in the half-tones is obtained. Wash 5 to 10 minutes after dyeing until the highlights are clear. The life of the double toning bath is the same as the iron toner (Formula T-11, page 132).

[Formula T-20] **Single Solution Dye Toner**

	Avoirdupois		Metric
*Dye	x ounces	x grains	x grams
Acetone or Wood Alcohol	11¾ gallons	3¼ fluid ozs.	100.0 cc.
Potassium Ferricyanide	1 pound	15 grains	1.0 gram
Acetic Acid (glacial) .	75 fluid ozs.	1¼ drams	5.0 cc.
Water to make . . . 120	gallons	32 ounces	1.0 liter

*The quantity of dye varies according to the dye used as follows:

	Avoirdupois		Metric
Safranine (Extra Bluish) .	3½ ounces	3 grains	0.2 gram
Chrysoidine 3R. . . .	3½ ounces	3 grains	0.2 gram
Auramine	7 ounces	6 grains	0.4 gram
Victoria Green	7 ounces	6 grains	0.4 gram
Rhodamine B	7 ounces	6 grains	0.4 gram

Note: The dyes listed are obtainable from the Eastman Kodak Co., Rochester, N. Y., in quantities under one pound.

The nature of the tone varies with time of toning and eventually a point is reached beyond which it is unsafe to continue as the gradation of the toned image becomes affected. Average toning time at 65° F. (18° C.) is from 3 to 9 minutes. Further details on the use of this formula may be obtained by referring to the paper by Crabtree and Ives.*

Tinting Slides or Films

Tinting consists of immersing a film or slide in a solution of an acid dye which colors the gelatin layer, causing the whole picture to have a veil of color over it. Motion picture positive films may be purchased in a variety of tinted bases which obviates the necessity for actual coloring.

Sheets of water colors or liquid water colors recommended for coloring photographs may be used for tinting slides or film transparencies. In the case of most colors the absorption of the color is hastened by the addition of one volume of glacial acetic acid to 1000 volumes of the dye solution. Bathing for 3 to 4 minutes in the acid dye solution is usually ample. After tinting, the slide should be rinsed in water for a few seconds and wiped off with a moist tuft of absorbent cotton. If the color is too strong, it should be washed in water or a 2 per cent solution of ammonia.

Pleasing effects may also be secured by combined tinting and toning such as a blue tone followed by an orange, red, or yellow tint. The clear portions or highlights thus assume the

*"Dye Toning With Single Solutions" by J. I. Crabtree and C. E. Ives, Trans. Soc. Mot. Pict. Eng. *12:* 967 (1928).

color of the tinting solution while the half-tones and shadows show a color intermediate between the tint and tone used.

Slides fixed in plain or acid hypo (Formula F-24, page 119) take colors better than those fixed in an acid hardening fixing bath.

B. Toning Baths for Paper Prints

Sepia Toning—Hypo-Alum Bath [Formula T-1a]
For Amateur and Professional Contact Papers

	Avoirdupois	Metric
Cold water	90 ounces	700.0 cc.
Sodium Thiosulfate (Hypo)	16 ounces	120.0 grams

Dissolve thoroughly, and add the following solution:

	Avoirdupois	Metric
Hot water (about 160° F.) (71° C.)	20 ounces	160.0 cc.
Potassium Alum (E.K.Co.)	4 ounces	30.0 grams

Then add the following solution (including precipitate) *slowly to the hypo-alum solution while stirring the latter rapidly.*

	Avoirdupois	Metric
Cold water	2 ounces	16.0 cc.
Silver Nitrate, crystals (E.K.Co.)	60 grains	1.1 grams
Sodium Chloride (table salt)	60 grains	1.1 grams

After combining above solutions.

	Avoirdupois	Metric
Add water to make	1 gallon	1.0 liter

Note: The silver nitrate should be dissolved completely before adding the sodium chloride and immediately afterward, the solution containing the milky white precipitate should be added to the hypo-alum solution as directed above.

For use, pour into a tray supported in a water bath. The toning bath should be heated to and maintained at 120° F. (49° C.) for best results. Dry prints should be soaked thoroughly in water before toning. Prints will tone in 12 to 15 minutes depending upon the grade of paper. Toning should not be continued longer than 20 minutes at 120° F. (49° C.).

The formation of a black or gray precipitate in the bath in no way impairs the toning action of the bath if proper manipulation technique is used.

Prints should be immersed thoroughly and separated occasionally, especially during the first few minutes to insure even toning. The untoned print should be slightly denser

(Over)

than normal and developed from 1½ to 2 minutes without forcing, to produce good sepia tones.

After prints are toned, sponge off any sediment in warm water and wash one hour in running water.

[Formula T-7a] **Sepia Re-developing Solution**
For Chloride and Bromide Papers

No. 1—Stock Bleaching Solution

	Avoirdupois	Metric
Potassium Ferricyanide	2½ ounces	75.0 grams
Potassium Bromide	2½ ounces	75.0 grams
Potassium Oxalate	6½ ounces	195.0 grams
*Acetic Acid (28% pure) (E.K.Co.)	1¼ fluid ozs.	40.0 cc.
Water	64 ounces	2.0 liters

*To make 28% acetic acid from glacial acetic acid, dilute 3 parts of glacial acid with 8 parts of water.

No. 2—Stock Re-developing Solution

Sodium Sulfide (not sulfite)	1½ ounces	45.0 grams
Water	16 ounces	500.0 cc.

Prepare Bleaching Bath as follows:

Stock Solution No. 1	16 ounces	500.0 cc.
Water	16 ounces	500.0 cc.

Prepare Re-developer as follows:

Stock Solution No. 2	4 ounces	125.0 cc.
Water	32 ounces	1.0 liter

Working Directions: Immerse print, which should first be washed thoroughly, in the Bleaching Bath, at 65° F. (18° C.) allowing it to remain until only faint traces of the half-tones are left and the black of the shadows has disappeared. This operation will take about one minute.

Note: Particular care should be taken *not* to use trays with any *iron* exposed, otherwise blue spots may result.

Rinse *thoroughly* in clean cold water as all chemicals must be removed.

Place in Re-developer Solution until original detail returns (for about 30 seconds). Immediately after the print leaves the Re-developer, rinse *thoroughly*, then immerse it for 5 minutes in a hardening bath composed of one part of the hardener recommended for the acid fixing bath (Formula F-1a, page 120) and 8 parts of water. Remove the print from this bath and wash for one-half hour in running water. The color and gradation of the finished print will not be affected by the use of this bath.

Nelson Gold Toning Bath
For Sepia Tones on Professional Contact and Enlarging Papers

[Formula T-21]

The feature of this toning bath is, that a variety of excellent brown tones may be obtained by varying the time of toning, that is, the prints may be removed at any time from the bath when a satisfactory color is obtained. For average results, toning will require about 5 to 20 minutes for professional papers according to the depth of tone desired. Contact papers in general, tone more rapidly than enlarging papers. After fixing, wash the prints for a few minutes before toning.

Stock Solution No. 1

	Avoirdupois	Metric
Warm water (about 125° F.) (52° C.)	1 gallon	4.0 liters
Sodium Thiosulfate (Hypo)	2 pounds	960.0 grams
Ammonium Persulfate	4 ounces	120.0 grams

Dissolve the hypo completely before adding the ammonium persulfate. Stir the bath vigorously while adding the ammonium persulfate. If the bath does not turn milky, increase the temperature until it does.

Prepare the following solution and add it (including precipitate) slowly to the hypo-persulfate solution while stirring the latter rapidly. *The bath must be cool when these solutions are added together.*

	Avoirdupois	Metric
Cold water	2 ounces	64.0 cc.
Silver Nitrate, crystals (E.K.Co.)	75 grains	5.2 grams
Sodium Chloride (table salt)	75 grains	5.2 grams

Note: The silver nitrate should be dissolved completely before adding the sodium chloride.

Stock Solution No. 2

	Avoirdupois	Metric
Water	8 ounces	250.0 cc.
Gold Chloride	15 grains	1.0 gram

For use, add 4 ounces (125 cc.) of solution No. 2 slowly to solution No. 1 while stirring the latter rapidly.

The bath should not be used until after it has become cold and has formed a sediment. Then pour off the clear liquid for use.

Add the clear solution to a tray supported in a water bath and heat to 110° F. (43° C.). The temperature, when toning should be between 100° and 110° F. (38° and 43° C.). Dry prints should be soaked thoroughly in water before toning.

Keep at hand an untoned black and white print for com-

(*Over*)

parison during toning. Prints should be separated at all times to insure even toning.

When the desired tone is obtained, rinse the prints in cold water. After all prints have been toned, return them to the fixing bath for 5 minutes, then wash for one hour in running water.

The bath should be revived at intervals by the addition of further quantities of the gold solution No. 2. The quantity to be added will depend upon the number of prints toned and the time of toning. For example, when toning to a warm brown, add one dram (4 cc.) of gold solution after each fifty, 8 x 10-inch prints or their equivalent have been toned. Fresh solution may be added from time to time to keep the bath up to the proper volume.

Color Toning with Uranium, Iron, and Dyes

Tones on paper may be obtained with uranium (Formula T-17) ranging from chocolate to brick red. This formula may also be used as a mordant bath for dye tones. The paper stock usually becomes tinted unless it is protected by squeegeeing temporarily to another support coated with rubber cement. Blue tones may be obtained with an iron toning bath (Formula T-12).

Toned images obtained with these formulas are not absolutely permanent since they consist of a mixture of silver with one or more of the following compounds: silver ferrocyanide, dye, ferric ferrocyanide, and uranyl ferrocyanide. On exposure to the atmosphere, which usually contains traces of hydrogen sulfide, the silver and uranyl ferrocyanides are converted to silver or uranyl sulfide which is usually apparent as a metallic sheen on the surface of the toned print. This sulfiding of the image can be prevented almost completely by varnishing the prints with a nitrocellulose lacquer.

In all these processes, the final tone depends not only on the time of toning but also on the density of the original print.

Important: It is very important to wash prints very thoroughly, at least two hours, if they are to be toned by any of the following methods. Traces of hypo in the paper will **cause inferior tones.**

Iron Toning Bath for Blue Tones [Formula T-12]

(Keep in a well-stoppered brown bottle)

	Avoirdupois	Metric
Ferric Ammonium Citrate (green scales)	58 grains	4.0 grams
Oxalic Acid, crystals	58 grains	4.0 grams
Potassium Ferricyanide	58 grains	4.0 grams
Water to make	32 ounces	1.0 liter

Dissolve each chemical separately in a small volume of water, about 8 ounces (250 cc.) and filter before mixing together.

Immerse the well-washed print in the toning bath for 10 to 15 minutes until the desired tone is obtained. Then wash until the highlights are clear.

Uranium Mordanting and Toning Bath [Formula T-17]

Stock Solution

	Avoirdupois	Metric
Uranium Nitrate	116 grains	8.0 grams
Oxalic Acid, crystals	58 grains	4.0 grams
Potassium Ferricyanide	58 grains	4.0 grams
Water to make	32 ounces	1.0 liter

Dissolve the uranium nitrate in a small volume of water, about 8 ounces (250 cc.) (about 125° F.) (52° C.). Dissolve the oxalic acid separately in about 8 ounces (250 cc.) of water and filter; then add the oxalic acid solution to the uranium nitrate solution. Dissolve the potassium ferricyanide separately in about 8 ounces (250 cc.) of water; if the solution is clear, add it to the uranium nitrate and oxalic acid solution. If not clear, filter before mixing together.

For Use as a Toning Bath (Chocolate to Brick Red). Dilute one part of the stock solution T-17 with 2 parts of water. As the toning time is increased, the tone changes from chocolate to brown and finally to brick red. The print may be removed at any stage.

Wash until the highlights are clean, which usually requires from 10 to 15 minutes.

For Use as a Mordant for Dye Toning. Dilute one part stock solution (T-17) with 4 parts of water.

Treat the well-washed print about 2 minutes until the image turns a light chocolate color. Rinse for about one minute or less in running water to remove the yellow stain from the highlights. Then immerse for 10 to 15 minutes in the following dye bath:

142 ELEMENTARY PHOTOGRAPHIC CHEMISTRY

[Formula T-17b]   **Dye Bath for Papers**

	Avoirdupois	Metric
Dye (1:1000 solution)	x fluid oz.	x cc.
Acetic Acid, 1% solution	6¾ fluid ozs.	25.0 cc.
Water to make	32 ounces	1.0 liter

Volumes of 1:1000 *Dye Solution for Various Colors

			Avoirdupois	Metric
Tone No. 1	Red	Safranine A	3¼ fluid ozs.	100.0 cc.
Tone No. 2	Yellow	Auramine	3¼ fluid ozs.	100.0 cc.
Tone No. 3	Orange		Use equal parts of Nos. 1 and 2, then add 3¼ fluid ounces (100 cc.) of the mixed dye solution when preparing the acid dye bath.	
Tone No. 4	Blue-Green	Victoria Green	3¼ fluid ozs.	100.0 cc.
Tone No. 5	Brilliant Green		Use equal parts of Nos. 2 and 4, then add 3¼ fluid ounces (100 cc.) of the mixed dye solution when preparing the acid dye bath.	
Tone No. 6	Blue	Methylene Blue BB	3¼ fluid ozs.	100.0 cc.
Tone No. 7	Violet	Methyl Violet	5½ fluid drams	20.0 cc.

Mixtures of the following may also be used:

Victoria Green plus Methyl Violet
Victoria Green plus Methylene Blue
Methyl Violet plus Auramine
Methyl Violet plus Victoria Green

The dye toned print should be washed in running water until all extraneous color is removed from the highlights.

*The 1 to 1000 stock solution of the dye is prepared by dissolving one part of dye in 1000 parts of water (one gram in one liter, or 15 grains in 32 ounces).

Note: The dyes listed are obtainable from the Eastman Kodak Co., Rochester, N. Y., in quantities under one pound.

[Formula S-6]   **Stain Remover**

Developer or oxidation stain may be removed by first hardening the film for 2 or 3 minutes in a 5% formalin solution, or in the alkaline formalin bath (SH-1), page 122, followed by rinsing in water and fixing in a fresh acid fixing bath. Then wash for 20 minutes and bleach in S-6 solution.

Stock Solution A

	Avoirdupois	Metric
Water	32 ounces	1.0 liter
Potassium Permanganate	75 grains	5.2 grams

Stock Solution B

	Avoirdupois	Metric
Cold water	16 ounces	500.0 cc.
Sodium Chloride (table salt)	2½ ounces	75.0 grams
Sulfuric Acid, C.P. (E.K.Co.)	½ fluid oz.	16.0 cc.
Water to make	32 ounces	1.0 liter

FORMULAS

Use equal parts of A and B. The solutions should not be mixed until ready for immediate use since they do not keep long after mixing. All particles of permanganate should be dissolved completely when preparing solution A, since undissolved particles are likely to produce spots on the negative. (See page 123 for best method of dissolving permanganate.)

Bleaching should be complete in 3 or 4 minutes at 65° F. (18° C.). The brown stain of manganese dioxide formed in the bleaching bath is best removed by immersing the negative in a 1% sodium bisulfite solution. Then rinse well and develop fully in strong light with any non-staining developer such as Formula D-72 diluted one part to 2 parts of water (see page 96).

Warning: Developers containing high sulfite and low alkali should not be used for re-development, because the sulfite tends to dissolve the silver image before the developer can act upon it.

After development, rinse the negatives for about one minute in the acetic acid rinse bath (SB-1, page 114) and wash for 20 to 30 minutes before drying.

Hand Stain Remover [Formula S-5]

Solution No. 1

	Avoirdupois	Metric
Water	32 ounces	1.0 liter
Potassium Permanganate	¼ ounce	7.5 grams

Solution No. 2

	Avoirdupois	Metric
Water	32 ounces	1.0 liter
Sodium Bisulfite (E.K.Co.)	16 ounces	480.0 grams

Rub the hands with a small volume of the No. 1 solution, rinse in water; then pour a small volume of the No. 2 solution in the palm of one hand. Rub it quickly over the hands and, when free from stain, wash thoroughly with water. If the original stain is not entirely removed, repeat the treatment with solutions 1 and 2.

If complete immersion of the hands in the No. 2 solution is desired, the solution should be diluted one part of No. 2 solution to 4 parts of water.

Tray Cleaner [Formula TC-1]
For General Use

	Avoirdupois	Metric
Water	32 ounces	1.0 liter
Potassium Bichromate	3 ounces	90.0 grams
Sulfuric Acid, C.P. (E.K.Co.)	3 fluid ozs.	96.0 cc.

(*Over*)

Add the sulfuric acid slowly while stirring the bichromate solution rapidly.

For use, pour a small volume of the tray cleaner solution in the vessel to be cleaned. Rinse around so that the solution has access to all parts of the tray; then pour the solution out and wash the tray six or eight times with water until all traces of the cleaning solution disappear.

This solution will remove stains caused by oxidation products of developers, some silver stains and dye stains, and is a very useful cleaning agent.

[Formula TC-2]

Tray Cleaner
For Removal of Silver Stains

Solution A

	Avoirdupois	Metric
Water	32 ounces	1.0 liter
Potassium Permanganate	73 grains	5.0 grams
*Sulfuric Acid, C.P. (E.K.Co.)	2½ drams	10.0 cc.

*Add the sulfuric acid slowly while stirring the permanganate solution rapidly. See directions on page 123 for dissolving permanganate crystals.

Solution B

	Avoirdupois	Metric
Water	32 ounces	1.0 liter
Sodium Bisulfite (E.K.Co.)	145 grains	10.0 grams

For use, pour Solution A into the tray and allow it to remain for a few minutes, then rinse with water. Apply Solution B, and wash thoroughly.

This formula is satisfactory for the removal of most types of general stains but it is especially recommended for the removal of silver stains.

Cleaning Deep Tanks

Use hypochlorite solution or paste as directed on pages 88 and 89.

FORMULA INDEX

Formula Number	Page	Description
		Developers for Films and Plates
D-1	95	Three Solution Pyro: For Tray or Tank Use.
D-7	95	Elon-Pyro Developer: For General Portrait and Commercial Use.
D-8	101	Single Solution: Hydroquinone-Caustic: Contrast.
D-9	102	Process Tray: Hydroquinone-Caustic Soda.
D-11	102	Process Tank or Tray: Elon-Hydroquinone.
D-13	103	Tropical Process: Kodelon-Hydroquinone.
D-16	107	Normal Positive Tank: Also for Variable Width Sound Negatives.
D-16R	107	Replenisher for D-16.
D-19	108	High Contrast: For Aero and Press Films, Wratten "M," Metallographic, Eastman Spectroscopic, and Infra-red Sensitive Plates.
D-32	110	Lantern Slide: Warm Black Tones.
D-61a	91	Elon-Hydroquinone: For General Tray or Tank Use.
D-61R	91	Replenisher Solution for D-61a.
D-72	96	Elon-Hydroquinone: For Press Photography and Lantern Slides.
D-76	94, 105	Elon-Hydroquinone-Borax: For Greatest Shadow Detail.
D-76R	94	Replenisher for D-76.
D-76c	109	Low and Normal Contrast: For Wratten "M" and Metallographic Plates.
D-76d	106	Buffered Borax.
D-78	106	Athenon (Glycin) Negative: Reel or Tank.
D-79	106	Pyro Tank: For Negative Motion Picture Film.
D-82	97	Maximum Energy: For High Speed Films or Plates.

Formula Number	Page	Description
D-84	97	Non-Staining Pyro Tray: For Transparencies, Copy Negatives and Ciné Enlargements.
D-85	103	Kodalith Film, Plate and Paper: For Line and Half-tone Negatives of Extreme Contrast.
D-85b	104	Two-Solution: For Kodalith Film, Plate and Paper.
D-87	108	Pyro: For Aero Film.
D-90	96	Two Solution Pyro Tray.
D-91	100	Kodelon Tropical.

Kodalk Developers

Formula Number	Page	Description
DK-15	99	Kodalk Tropical: (Non-blistering).
DK-20	93	Kodak Fine Grain for General Use.
DK-20R	93	Replenisher for DK-20.
DK-50	92	Kodalk: For Professional Films and Plates.
DK-50R	92	Replenisher for DK-50.
DK-60a	98	Kodalk: For General Tank Use and Machine Development of Roll Films and Film Packs.
DK-60aTR	98	Replenisher for DK-60a for Tank Development.
DK-60aMR	99	Replenisher for DK-60a for Machine Use.
DK-60b	107	Kodalk: Fast Aero Film.
DK-93	97	Kodelon-Hydroquinone-Kodalk: For General Use with Films and Plates.
SD-12	109	Special: For Autopositive Film.

Developers for Papers

Formula Number	Page	Description
D-51	111	Amidol: For Bromide Papers.
D-52	110	Portrait Paper.
D-72	111	Universal Paper: For Amateur Contact Prints and Enlargements.
D-88	112	For Direct Positive Prints.

Formula Number	Page	Description
		Hardening and Rinse Baths
SB-1 .	114	Acid Rinse: For Papers.
SB-1a .	114	Acid Rinse: For Kodalith Films, Plates and Paper and Kodalith Stripping Film (Normal).
SB-3 .	114	Chrome Alum Hardener: For Films and Plates.
SB-4 .	114	Tropical Hardener: For Films and Plates.
SB-5 .	115	Acetic Acid—Sulfate Non-swelling Rinse for Roll Film.
SH-1 .	122	Formalin Hardener: For Films and Plates.
		Fixing Baths
F-1 . .	119	Acid Hardening Fixing: For Papers.
F-1a .	120	Stock Hardener for F-1.
F-5 . .	115	Acid Hardening Fixing: For General Use with Films, Plates and Papers.
F-5a .	116	Stock Hardener for F-5.
F-6 . .	116	Odorless Acid Fixing Bath.
F-6a. .	116	Stock Hardener for F-6.
F-10 .	117	Acid Hardening Fixing: For Use with Highly Alkaline Developers.
F-16 .	117	Chrome Alum Fixing: For Films and Plates.
F-23 .	118	Chrome Alum Fixing: For Motion Picture Films. For Use at 75° to 90°F. (24° to 32°C.).
F-24 .	119	Non-Hardening Fixing.
F-25 .	118	Acid Hardening Fixing: For Motion Picture Films.
F-25a .	119	Stock Hardener for F-25.
		Washing Test and Hypo Eliminator
HT-1a .	120	Hypo Test Solution.
HE-1 .	121	Hypo Eliminator
		Reducers
R-1 . .	126	Persulfate: For Correcting Overdeveloped Negatives of Contrasty Subjects.

Formula Number	Page	Description
R-2	122	Permanganate: For Correcting Overexposed Negatives.
R-4	123	Farmer's: For Amateur Use for Correcting Overexposed Negatives.
R-4a	124	Farmer's: For all Professional Films and Plates; for Correcting Overexposed Negatives.
R-4b	124	Farmer's Two-Solution: For Correcting Overdeveloped Negatives.
R-5	125	Proportional: For Correcting Overdeveloped Negatives.
R-7	125	Ferric Alum Proportional: For Correcting Overdeveloped Motion Picture Negatives.
R-8	126	Modified Belitski: For Correcting Overexposed and Overdeveloped Negatives.
R-9	113	Bleaching Bath: For Direct Positives.
CB-1	113	Clearing Bath: For Direct Positives.

Intensifiers

In-1	126	Mercury. (Monckhoven's).
In-4	127	Chromium: Stock Solution.
In-5	128	Silver: For General Use on Films or Plates.

Toning Negatives

T-9	130	Uranium Toner: For Brown to Red Tones on Slides or Films.
T-10	131	Sulfide Toner: For Sepia Tones on Lantern Slides.
T-10a	131	Sulfide Toner: For Sepia Tones on Motion Picture Film.
T-11	132	Iron Toner: For Blue Tones on Slides or Films.
T-12	141	Iron Toner: For Blue Tones on Papers.

Formula Number	Page	Description
T-17	133	Uranium Mordanting Bath.
	134	Copper Mordanting Bath (Chalkley Formula).
T-17a	134	Dye Bath.
T-17b	142	Dye Bath for Papers.
T-18	135	Double Toning Bath.
T-20	136	Single Solution Dye Toner.

Toning Paper Prints

T-1a	137	Sepia Toning—Hypo Alum Bath: For Amateur and Professional Contact Papers.
T-7a	138	Sepia Re-developing Solution: For Chloride and Bromide Papers.
T-17	141	Uranium Mordanting and Toning Bath.
T-19	113	Sulfide Re-developer: For Direct Positives.
T-21	139	Nelson Gold Toning Bath: For Sepia Tones on Professional Contact and Enlarging Papers.

Stain Remover

S-5	143	Hand Stain Remover.
S-6	142	Stain Remover: For Negatives.

Tray Cleaner

TC-1	143	For General Use.
TC-2	144	For Removal of Silver Stains.
	88	For Deep Tanks.

APPROXIMATE KEEPING PROPERTIES (WITHOUT USE) AND LIFE OF SOLUTIONS MADE FROM EASTMAN FORMULAS

The tables on pages 151 and 152 give the approximate keeping properties and useful capacities of solutions made from Eastman formulas. The values for keeping properties without use are for 65° to 70° F. (18° to 21° C.) and are proportionately less at higher temperatures. They are also decreased by agitation of the solutions.

The values given are merely estimates based on experience and are intended for use only as a guide. The useful capacity values are based on exhaustion of the solution *without replenishment*. For negative developers, the figures represent the number of films, or plates, that may be developed before the effective emulsion speed has dropped to approximately 75 per cent of the value in the fresh developer.

The capacity of a developer is usually somewhat greater if it is used continuously rather than intermittently. The values given represent continuous use soon after mixing. The chief factors affecting the useful capacity or quantity of film (paper) which can be processed per unit volume of solution are: (1) Nature of the emulsion; (2) Area of solution exposed to the air and susceptibility of the solution to aerial oxidation; (3) Degree of agitation; (4) Time of storage with and without use; (5) Contamination or replenishing effect resulting from pretreatment of material in another solution; (6) Temperature; (7) Degree of dilution.

Keeping Properties of Solutions

	Keeping Properties Without Use				Useful Life 8 x 10-inch Sheets per Gallon		
			Stoppered Bottle			Narrow	
Formula	8 x 10 Tray	Gallon Tank	Full	Half Full	8 x 10 Tray	and Deep Tank	Purpose
D-1	30 Min.	3 Hrs.	1 Mo. S.S.	2 Wks. S.S.	10	20	Neg.
D-7	8 Hrs.	1 Wk.	3 Mo. S.S.	2 Mo. S.S.	10	20	Neg.
D-8	4 Hrs.	N.R.	2 Mo.	1 Mo.	15	30	Neg.
D-11	24 Hrs.	1 Mo.	6 Mo.	1 Mo.	20	40	Neg.
SD-12	8 Hrs.	1 Wk.	1 Mo.	2 Wks.	20	40	Dup.
D-13	4-8 Hrs.	2 Wks.	2 Mo.	1 Wk.	15	30	Neg.
DK-15	8 Hrs.	1 Wk.	3 Mo.	1 Mo.	15	30	Neg.
D-16	24 Hrs.	1 Mo.	6 Mo.	2 Mo.	20	40	Neg.
D-19	24 Hrs.	1 Mo.	6 Mo.	2 Mo.	30	60	Neg.
DK-20	24 Hrs.	1 Mo.	6 Mo.	2 Mo.	20	30*	Neg.
D-32	2 Hrs.	N.R.	2 Mo. S.S.	2 Wks. S.S.	15	N.R.	L.S.
DK-50	24 Hrs.	1 Mo.	6 Mo.	2 Mo.	20	40*	Neg.
D-51	2 Hrs.	1 Day	..	..	40	N.R.	Pr.
D-52	24 Hrs.	2 Wks.	3 Mo.	1 Mo.	{40(F.S.) / 30(1:1)}	N.R.	Pr.
DK-60a	24 Hrs.	1½ Mo.	6 Mo.	2 Mo.	20	40*	Neg.
DK-60b	24 Hrs.	1 Mo.	6 Mo.	2 Mo.	20	40*	Neg.
D-61a	24 Hrs.(1:1)	2 Wks.(1:3)	2 Mo.	3 Wks.	15(1:1)	30(1:3)	Neg.
D-72	24 Hrs.	2 Wks.	3 Mo.	1 Mo.	{20(1:1) / 15(1:2) / 30(1:1) / 30(1:2) / 20(1:4)}	{40(1:1) / 30(1:2) / .. / .. / ..}	{Neg. / Pr. / L.S.}
D-76	24 Hrs.	1 Mo.	6 Mo.	2 Mo.	10	10*	Neg.
D-76c	24 Hrs.	1 Mo.	6 Mo.	2 Mo.	10	10*	Neg.
D-76d	24 Hrs.	1 Mo.	6 Mo.	2 Mo.	10	10*	Neg.
D-78	24 Hrs.	1 Mo.	6 Mo.	2 Mo.	10	10*	Neg.
D-79	N.R.	4 Hrs.	..	..	N.R.	10	Neg.
D-82	2 Hrs.	24 Hrs.	1 Wk.	2 Days	10	20	Neg.
D-84	30 Min.	3 Hrs.	1 Mo. S.S.	2 Wks. S.S.	10	20	Neg.
D-85	4 Hrs.	N.R.	1 Mo.	3 Days	25	40	Neg.
D-85b	4 Hrs.	N.R.	3 Mo. S.S.	3 Wks.	25	40	Neg.
D-87	15 Min.	1 Hr.	..	..	N.R.	10	Neg.
D-90	30 Min.	3 Hrs.	1 Mo. S.S.	2 Wks. S.S.	10	20	Neg.
D-91	24 Hrs.	1 Mo.	6 Mo.	2 Mo.	20	40	Neg.
DK-93	24 Hrs.	1 Mo.	6 Mo.	2 Mo.	20	40	Neg.

*Life extended greatly by addition of the proper replenisher.

Keeping Properties of Solutions—Continued

	Keeping Properties Without Use				Useful Life 8 x 10-inch Sheets per Gallon	
			Stoppered Bottle		8 x 10	Narrow and Deep
Formula	8 x 10 Tray	Gallon Tank	65° F.	75° F.	Tray	Tank
Stop Baths						
SB-1	3 Days	1 Mo.	Indef.	Indef.	75	75
SB-1a	3 Days	1 Mo.	Indef.	Indef.	40 (Used with D-8)	40
SB-3	1 Day	1 Mo.	Indef.	Indef.	25	25
SB-4	1 Day	1 Mo.	Indef.	Indef.	25	25
SB-5	3 Days	1 Mo.	Indef.	Indef.	100	100
Fixing Bath						
F-1	1 Wk.	1 Mo.	3 Mo.	1 Wk.	{ 60(W.R.) 120(SB-1)	60* 120
F-5	1 Wk.	1 Mo.	3 Mo.	2 Wks.	{ 100(W.R.) 100(SB-3)	100* 100
F-6	1 Wk.	2 Mo.	3 Mo.	3 Wks.	{ 50(W.R.) 100(SB-1)	50 100
F-10	1 Wk.	2 Mo.	3 Mo.	3 Wks.	{ 100(W.R.) 100(SB-3)	100 100
F-16	3 Days	1 Wk.	1 Wk.	1-2 Days	{ 50(W.R.) 75(SB-3)	50* 75
F-23	3 Days	1 Wk.	1 Wk.	1-2 Days	{ 50(W.R.) 75(SB-3)	50* 75
F-24	1 Wk.	1 Wk.	3 Mo.	2 Wks.	{ 50(W.R.) 75(SB-3)	50 75
F-25	3 Days	2 Wks.	1 Mo.	1 Wk. (2 Wks. with double sulfite)	60	60

FS—Full Strength
SS—Stock Solution in separate bottles
N.R.—Not recommended
*W.R.—Water rinse between development and fixing
S.B.—Stop bath between development and fixing

Neg.—Negatives
Dup.—Duplicates
Pr.—Prints
L. S.—Lantern Slides

Equivalents for use in determining the useful life of processing solutions in terms of roll films.

2 rolls No. 127 is approximately equal to 1   8 x 10-inch sheet of cut film
1 roll No. 135 is approximately equal to 1   8 x 10-inch sheet of cut film
1 roll No. 120 is approximately equal to 1   8 x 10-inch sheet of cut film
1 roll No. 116 is approximately equal to 1½   8 x 10-inch sheets of cut film
1 roll No. 122 is approximately equal to 2   8 x 10-inch sheets of cut film

EQUIVALENT WEIGHTS OF CHEMICALS

The formulas in this book call for Kodak desiccated Sodium Carbonate, Sodium Sulfite, and Sodium Sulfate. It is preferable to use these chemicals because of their purity and known strength. However, crystalline forms can be used if the weight taken is increased to allow for the water of crystallization present.

Sodium Carbonite

 100 parts desiccated = 117 parts monohydrated
         = 270 parts crystalline

Sodium Sulfite

 100 parts desiccated = 200 parts crystalline

Sodium Sulfate

 100 parts desiccated = 230 parts crystalline

To Make 28% Acetic Acid

 Dilute 3 parts of glacial acetic acid with 8 parts of water.
 Dilute 7 parts of 80% acetic acid with 13 parts of water.
 Dilute one part of 56% acetic acid with one part of water.

TIME-TEMPERATURE DEVELOPMENT TABLES

Maintaining Proper Negative Contrast at Different Temperatures:

In warm weather, many photographers find it difficult to maintain the temperature of developing solutions at the normal level of 65° F. (18° C.). Unless the development time is adjusted to compensate for this departure from normal temperature, the resulting negatives will be more contrasty than usual.

Tables of development times at various temperatures are given below for several of the more commonly used Eastman Developer Formulas, which apply for most negative emulsions. In order to allow for varying standards of desired contrast, each table contains several columns corresponding to different development times at 65° F. (18° C.). Figures are included for temperatures from 55° F. to 75° F. (12.5° to 24° C.), which are just about the limits of useful developing temperatures. At lower temperatures, development is too slow to be practical, and at higher temperatures there is danger of the emulsion softening.

In order to use the table for the developer in use, find the development time at 65° F. (18° C.) which gives the desired contrast in the line opposite 65° F. (18° C.) then the figures in the same column, above and below this time, show the development times which give this contrast at various other temperatures. Since figures are given for five degree intervals of temperature, it may be necessary to estimate between the values given to obtain the development times for intermediate temperatures.

D-7 (1:1:1:8)

Temperature	Time of Development (minutes)						
75° F.	3½	4¼	5	5¾	6½	7¼	8
70°	4¼	5	6	6¾	7¾	8½	9¼
65°	5	6	7	8	9	10	11
60°	6	7	8¼	9½	10½	11¾	13
55°	7	8¼	9¾	11	12½	14	15¼

D-11

75°	2¼	2½	2¾	3	3½	3¾
70°	2¾	3	3½	4	4¼	4¾
65°	3½	4	4½	5	5½	6
60°	4½	5	5¾	6¼	7	7½
55°	5¾	6½	7¼	8	8¾	9½

D-19

Temperature	Time of Development (minutes)					
75° F.	2¼	3	3½	4¼	5	5¾
70°	2½	3½	4¼	5	6	6¾
65°	3	4	5	6	7	8
60°	3½	4¾	6	7	8¼	9½
55°	4¼	5½	7	8¼	9¾	11

DK-20

75°	6	8½	11	13	15½	18
70°	8	11	14	17	20	23½
65°	10	14	18	22	26	30
60°	13	18	23	28	33	39
55°	17	23	30	36	43	50

DK-50

75°	3½	4¼	5	5¾	6½	7¼	8	8¾
70°	4¼	5	6	6¾	7¾	8½	9½	10¼
65°	5	6	7	8	9	10	11	12
60°	5¾	7	8¼	9¼	10½	11¾	13	14
55°	7	8¼	9¾	11	12½	13¾	15	16½

DK-60a

75°	3½	4	4½	5	5¾	6½
70°	4½	5¼	6	7	7¾	8½
65°	6	7	8	9	10	11
60°	8	9½	10½	12	13½	15
55°	10½	12½	14	16	17½	19½

D-61a (1:3)

75°	4	5¼	6½	7¾	9	10½	11¾
70°	4¾	6½	8	9½	11½	13	14½
65°	6	8	10	12	14	16	18
60°	7½	10	12½	15	17½	20	22½
55°	9¼	12½	15½	18½	22	25	28

D-61a (1:1)

75°	3¼	4	4½	5¼	5¾	6½	7¼
70°	4	4¾	5½	6½	7¼	8	8¾
65°	5	6	7	8	9	10	11
60°	6¼	7½	8¾	10	11¼	12½	13¾
55°	7¾	9¼	11	12½	14	15½	17

D-72 (1:2)

75°	1¾	2	2¼	2½	3¼	4	4½
70°	2	2½	2¾	3¼	4	4¾	5½
65°	2½	3	3½	4	5	6	7
60°	3	3¾	4½	5	6¼	7½	8¾
55°	4	4¾	5½	6¼	7¾	9¼	10¾

D-76

75°	6	7¼	9	10¾	12½	14½
70°	7¾	9¼	11½	14	16	18½
65°	10	12	15	18	21	24
60°	13	15½	19½	23	27	31
55°	17	20	25	30	35	40

TABLE OF CHEMICAL SOLUBILITIES

The following table will serve as a guide when preparing stock solutions of photographic chemicals. Since a solution is apt to become cooled in winter to a temperature approximating 40° F., it is not advisable to prepare a stock solution stronger than is indicated by the solubility of the chemical at this temperature.

Substance	Ounces of chemical in 100 ozs. (fluid) of Saturated Solution at 40°F.(4.4°C.)	70°F.(21°C.)
Acid, Acetic (any strength)	Mixes in all proportions	
Acid, Boric	3½	5
Acid, Citric	78	88
Acid, Oxalic	7¼	14½
Acid, Tartaric (dextro)	73	78
Alum, Ammonium	6¼	15½
Alum, Iron (Ferric)	48	59
Alum, Potassium	6¼	11½
Alum, Potassium Chrome	15½	20½
Amidol (See Diaminophenol Hydrochloride)		
Ammonia Solution	Mixes in all proportions	
Ammonium Bromide	52	57
Ammonium Carbonate	26	31
Ammonium Chloride	26	30
Ammonium Iodide	104	109
Ammonium Oxalate	2¾	5¼
Ammonium Persulfate	52	62
Ammonium Thiocyanate or Ammonium Sulfocyanide	62	73
Ammonium Thiosulfate, anhydrous	83	88
Athenon (para-hydroxyphenyl glycin)	Insol. in water; soluble in alkalies and sulfite	
Borax (Sodium Tetraborate)	2½	7¼
Boric Acid	3½	5
Caustic Potash (See Potassium Hydroxide)		
Caustic Soda (See Sodium Hydroxide)		
Copper Sulfate, crystal	26	31
Di-Aminophenol Hydrochloride (Amidol)	20½	26
Elon (Monomethyl para-Aminophenol Sulfate)	5¼	8¼
Ferric Alum (See Alum, Iron)		
Ferric Ammonium Citrate	Very soluble	Decomposes on standing
Ferric Chloride	113	131
Ferrous Sulfate	29	41
Formalin	Mixes in all proportions	
Glycin (See Athenon)		
Gold Chloride	79	Over 100
Hydroquinone	4¼	6¾
Hypo (See Sodium Thiosulfate)		
Kodalk	24	34
Kodelon (See Para-Aminophenol Hydrochloride)		
Lead Acetate	31	47

Substance	Ounces of chemical in 100 ozs. (fluid) of Saturated Solution at 40°F.(4.4°C.)	70°F.(21°C.)
Lead Nitrate	39½	51
Mercuric Chloride	4	6¼
Para-Aminophenol Hydrochloride (Kodelon)	1¼	2½
Para-Oxyphenyl Glycin (See Athenon)		
Potassium Bichromate	6¾	14½
Potassium Bromide	50	56
Potassium Carbonate, anhydrous	83	85
Potassium Chloride	26	31
Potassium Citrate	93	104
Potassium Cyanide	46	52
Potassium Ferricyanide	30	36
Potassium Ferrocyanide	17½	26
Potassium Hydroxide (Caustic Potash)	78	83
Potassium Iodide	99	104
Potassium Metabisulfite	47	57
Potassium Oxalate	29	36½
Potassium Permanganate	3¼	
Pyrogallic Acid (Pyro)	36	57
Rochelle Salts (See Sodium, Potassium Tartrate)		
Silver Nitrate	109	135
Sodium Acetate, anhydrous	31	36
Sodium Acetate, crystal (trihydrate)	52	62
Sodium Bicarbonate	7¼	9¼
Sodium Bisulfite	52	52
Sodium Bromide	67	73
Sodium Carbonate, anhydrous	10¼	24
Sodium Carbonate, monohydrated	12½	29¼
Sodium Carbonate, crystal	29	65
Sodium Chloride	31	31
Sodium Cyanide	25	48
Sodium Hydroxide (Caustic Soda)	50	83
Sodium Phosphate, dibasic crystal	6½	24
Sodium Phosphate, tribasic crystal	10¼	21½
Sodium, Potassium Tartrate (Rochelle Salts)	51	74
Sodium Sulfate, anhydrous	5¼	20½
Sodium Sulfate, crystal	10¼	41
Sodium Sulfide, fused	13½	17¾
Sodium Sulfide, crystal	36¼	47
Sodium Sulfite, anhydrous	17½	28
Sodium Tetraborate (See Borax)		
Sodium Thiosulfate, (Hypo) crystal	73	93
Thiourea	7¾	11¾
Uranyl (Uranium) Nitrate	114	130
Wood Alcohol (Methyl Alcohol)	Mixes in all proportions	

SUBJECT INDEX

	Page
Apparatus	55
Bromide in Developers	14, 19
Chemicals	
Storage of	69
Table of Solubilities	156
Chemistry	
Outline of Elementary	5
Of Photographic Materials	12
Cleaning Containers for Solutions	88
Conversion Tables	51, 86
Compounds, Types of	11
Cyanide	38
Deliquescence	69
Developers	
Alkalis in	20
Ammonia in	21
Basic Ingredients of	60
Bromide, effect of	14, 19
Chemistry of	17
Concentrated, mixing	65
Developing Agents in	18
Energy of	19
Mixing	60, 62
Preservatives in	25
Reduction potential	19
Restrainers in	19
Troubles	75
Two Solution	66, 73
Useful Life of	73, 151
Efflorescence	70
Elements	5
Emulsion, Definition of	12
Equivalent Weights of Chemicals	153
Exhaustion of Solutions	53
Farmer's Reducer	36, 45
Ferricyanide	36, 43, 44
Fixing Baths	
Acid in	28
Chemistry of	27
Chrome Alum	29
Formalin in	30
Hardening Agents in	28, 29
Hardening Action in	79

	Page
How to Prepare	66
Hypo in	27
Hypo Test	35, 37, 120
Mixing	66
Preservative in	28
Properties of	79
Purpose of	27
Recovery of Silver from	81
Troubles	82
Types of	66
Useful Life of	80
Fogging	84, 86
Formulas	90
Conversion of	51
Terminology and Arrangement of	54

(*Formula Index, pages 145-149*)

Gelatin	15, 28
Halides	9, 14
Hardening Agents	16, 29
Hydrometer, Use in Testing	52
Hypo—(See Fixing Baths)	
Hypo-Alum Toning	45
Intensification	
Chemistry of	39
Definition of	39
Keeping Properties of Solutions	150
Kodalk	24, 57
Kodapaint	56, 71
Life of Developers	73, 74, 151
Materials, Chemistry of Photographic	12
Measures and Weights	50
Mercury Intensification	40
Mixing Operations	56, 60, 62, 65, 67
Monckhoven's Intensifier	41
Nelson's Gold Toning Bath	47
Permanganate	37, 39
Persulfate	39
Printing-Out Papers	13
Reducers, Chemical	17
Reduction	
Chemistry of	36
Classification	36
Definition of	36

	Page
Proportional Reducers	39
Subtractive Reducers	36
Super Proportional Reducers	39
Rinsing, Importance of	77
Sepia—(See Toning)	
Silver Bromide	14
Silver Nitrate	9, 13
Silver, Recovery of (See Fixing Baths)	
Silver Sulfide	46, 48
Solubilities, Table of Chemical	156
Solutions	
Definition of	49
Keeping Properties of	150
Mixing	56, 60, 67
Percentage	53
Preparing	49
Removal of Particles from	58
Stock	53
Using	72
Storage of Chemicals	69
Tank Covers	67
Temperature	
Coefficient	86
Conversion	86
Effect on Chemicals and Solutions	85
Test for Hypo	37
Time-Temperature Developing Tables	154
Toning	
Chemistry of	42
Deposition of Salts	43
Dye Added to Image	45
Methods of	42
Replacement of Silver by Other Metal	42
Silver Sulfide (Sepia)	46
Uranium	39, 45
Washing	
Chemistry of	32
Contamination during	35
Rate of	32
Time of	34
Water Supply	59
Weights and Measures	50
Weights, equivalent, of chemicals	153

EASTMAN KODAK COMPANY
ROCHESTER, N. Y.